SEED AND POTTING
COMPOSTS

by W. J. C. Lawrence
PRACTICAL PLANT BREEDING
3rd Edition

THE YOUNG GARDENER
3rd Impression
(George Allen & Unwin)

by M. B. Crane and W. J. C. Lawrence
THE GENETICS OF GARDEN PLANTS
(Macmillan)

SCIENCE AND THE GLASSHOUSE
(Oliver & Boyd)

A collection of 100 species of stove plants all growing in the John Innes Potting Compos

SEED AND POTTING COMPOSTS

WITH SPECIAL REFERENCE TO SOIL STERILIZATION

By

W. J. C. LAWRENCE

*Curator, John Innes Horticultural
Institution, Merton*

and

J. NEWELL

*Assistant Curator,
John Innes Horticultural
Institution,
Merton*

ILLUSTRATED

LONDON
GEORGE ALLEN & UNWIN LTD

FIRST PUBLISHED IN 1939
REVISED SECOND EDITION, 1941
THIRD IMPRESSION (REVISED SECOND EDITION), 1942
FOURTH IMPRESSION (REVISED SECOND EDITION), 1943
REVISED THIRD EDITION, 1945
SIXTH IMPRESSION (REVISED THIRD EDITION), 1946
SEVENTH IMPRESSION (REVISED THIRD EDITION), 1948

PRINTED IN 12 POINT PERPETUA TYPE
IN GREAT BRITAIN BY
C. TINLING & CO., LTD.
LIVERPOOL, LONDON AND PRESCOT

FOREWORD

By Sir DANIEL HALL, k.c.b., f.r.s., ll.d.

THE first task of the scientific man who is working on behalf of any of the arts or crafts is to try to standardize the processes which the best practitioners carry out with such eminent success. Their success is the fruit of long experience and an observant mind, they find it difficult to describe why they do this or choose that; they arrive by a sort of intuition. Others seem to follow in their footsteps but do not get such good results, occasionally even the old hand has a failure. The aim of science is to replace this hard-won experience by something that is both more definite and more certain, for it is a maxim of science that a thing is not true until it can be repeated at will.

It is this sort of science that Mr. Lawrence and Mr. Newell are describing in their little book. It has always been good gardening practice to make up a compost for indoor work out of loam (by which the gardener means the top spit of an old pasture rotted down) and leaf mould and sand. But loam is by no means always the same thing; in some loams fine sand, in others clay predominates; sometimes they are acid with the accumulation of certain products of decay. Leaf mould is even more variable, according to the trees under which it has accumulated, and even sand may be coarse or fine, sharp or water worn. Then of late years a new disturbing factor has been introduced by the process of partial sterilization in order to get

rid of various harmful organisms. As the authors recount
in the preface, when they began to use sterilization
they had a series of unsatisfactory results, especially
as regards germination. Such partial failures would not
be liked in commercial work, but in plant-breeding
experiments, where the results will be valueless
unless every healthy seed produces its plant, they
cannot be tolerated. So Mr. Lawrence and Mr. Newell
set themselves to find the sources of failure. They
took the compost to pieces, as it were, and tested the
part played by each constituent by series of experiments
in which its nature and amount were varied. Similarly
the effect of each of the fertilizing materials and the
different ways of supplying lime were tested, with
and without sterilization. The experiments ran into
thousands; each step was made secure before going on
a stage, until in the end they have arrived at a couple
of composts which fulfil the definition I have given
of being scientific—they will give the same results
every time they are tried. They are not only standard
composts but I have every reason to believe they are
optimum composts which will give as far as the soil
goes the best possible results.

The book is so clearly written and the authors have
been so careful to think of every possible "crab" that
I regard their work as one of the most exact and
valuable pieces of science applied to horticulture that
has fallen within my experience.

PREFACE TO SECOND EDITION

WHEN this book first appeared in 1939, we presented the results of our experiments together with a little information from outside. In the succeeding two years we have not only extended our own experiments but have received reports from a considerable number of growers. We now possess, in addition to our own experimental results, detailed information on the behaviour of a variety of plants and crops when grown on a large scale by the John Innes methods. This information has been worked up into a new chapter (8 : the John Innes Composts). Other additions and alterations are as follows: Chapter 7, rearranged; Chapter 9, summarized at the end; Chapter 10, a section on the John Innes sterilizer has been included and the chapter summarized; Chapter 12, a new formula is given for the John Innes Feed. The list of plants at the end of the book has also been extended.

PREFACE

THIS is not a book about all kinds of composts but about two composts for all kinds of plants. These composts are the outcome of experiments to meet the practical needs of cultivation at the John Innes Horticultural Institution at Merton, England.

Large numbers of chinese primulas had been grown annually for twenty years with almost complete freedom from disease, but in 1933 a mysterious wilt appeared and out of a crop of 9,000 plants, 1,000 died. The evidence suggested a soil-borne organism was responsible, and as a precautionary measure " sterilized " soil was used for the 1934 crop. To our consternation the use of sterilized soil caused bad seed germination and unsatisfactory seedling growth and did not eliminate the wilt. Text books were consulted and enquiries made among growers, but no satisfactory explanation was found to account for this unexpected behaviour. Very soon it became clear that no proper investigations had been made concerning the most fundamental of all inside gardening operations, namely, the preparation of seed and potting composts. Composting depended purely on tradition and had no real experimental basis.

Accordingly we set to work to find out the facts for ourselves. Why did sterilization of the soil have such

detrimental effects on germination and young seedlings?
What were the essential characteristics of a good
compost, and what were the best materials to use ?
Could stable manure be dispensed with? These and
other important questions were answered one by
one and the field of enquiry widened to include the
feeding of pot plants, matters of general glasshouse
hygiene and the measures which could be taken to
simplify and standardize the business of growing
plants under glass.

This book contains our answers to these questions
and shows how the results of our experiments may be
applied in practice. In the past, failure to grow
healthy, vigorous plants has been attributed to all
kinds of irrelevant causes. So many unstandardized
conditions prevailed that the gardener had no means of
deciding to what his failure might be due, bad loam,
bad leaf-mould, bad composting, etc.

All this is now altered. In the John Innes composts
the gardener has soil mixtures which, properly used,
will always give excellent results. To make these
composts, neither expensive materials nor elaborate
and tiresome methods are needed. On the contrary,
composting is now an extremely simple job which
requires no stable manure, and which the most
inexperienced person can manage with ease. By
following the instructions given, the amateur can be

sure of growing first rate plants at a low cost; while the commercial or municipal grower may confidently rely on getting as good as or better results than before, with greater economy.

That there is a real need for simple standardized composts is shown by the surprisingly large number of enquiries we have received asking for more information on the subject. It is in response to these enquiries that we have endeavoured to present a simple, but comprehensive account of the principles and technique of composting for pot plants.

We are indebted to Sir Daniel Hall for much advice and helpful criticism and to Messrs. H. C. Osterstock and A. F. Emarton for preparing the illustrations.

CONTENTS

LIST OF ILLUSTRATIONS

SEED AND POTTING COMPOSTS

CHAPTER I

THE OLD COMPLEXITY

GARDENING is generally spoken of as an art and not as a science. To a great extent this is true, for we all know that given exactly the same plant, the same soil and the same environment one man will grow plants twice as good as those of a less able competitor or produce twice the crop. Actually the methods employed may differ very little and consist mainly in minor adjustments of temperature, moisture, etc. Nevertheless these differences, small in themselves, materially affect the final result. They are the consequence of a more or less sympathetic understanding of the requirements of plants under varying conditions —an understanding acquired only after years of experience.

The gardener observes that he gets a better result if he does this or that in some particular way, and this knowledge is stored in his mind, often subconsciously, and becomes part of his general understanding of the cultivation of plants. It is a slow way of learning and consists essentially in gaining knowledge from what are really unplanned trial and error experiments. It is knowledge which can only be passed on with difficulty because it rests on a large number of half remembered observations, mostly unconnected and without any exact basis of comparison. It is clear that planned experiments should enable the gardener to arrive at the principles underlying the culture of pot plants with greater precision and certainty, thus replacing the slow and uncertain rule of thumb practices by the more rapid and certain scientific methods.

What are the fundamental factors governing the cultivation of pot plants? They are firstly, an abundance of light, secondly a free circulation of air and thirdly soil which is well aerated, is easily penetrated by roots, has good moisture-retaining capacity, provides an adequate and balanced supply of plant food and is free from organisms and substances harmful to growth. These factors are the same for all plants, whether grown outdoors or under glass, but in the latter case we have much better control of them.

Hitherto this control has not been used to the best advantage in the preparation of seed and potting composts and in feeding pot plants. Many improvements have been made in horticultural materials and appliances and even greater improvements in the plants themselves, but composts and methods of composting remain practically unchanged from those in vogue at the end of the last century. Thus seed and potting composts are still made from a large number of materials including loam, leaf-soil, manure and sand, and in widely varying proportions according to the species, the age of the plant and the season at which it is grown. Whether such variation is necessary is clearly open to doubt. Comparison between the composts used shows that a plant is often grown equally well by different gardeners using different proportions of the same materials. A typical example is afforded by the Lorraine begonia. One gardener may use heavy loam lightened by about 10 per cent. of leaf-soil and animal manure, while another will use a light loam to which is added as much as 80 per cent. of humus, yet each will grow equally good plants. Extreme variations such as this may be unusual but even so we seldom find different growers using the same compost for any given plant. Further, in the same garden different composts made from varying proportions of the same materials are often used for each kind of plant grown. Thus most gardeners mix a compost for *Gloxinia* entirely different from that for *Schizanthus*.

It is impossible to find sound reasons for this practice of varying the compost proportions and ingredients. Indeed the very fact that equally good results can be obtained using composts varying both in the character and proportions of their ingredients suggests that it should be possible to mix up a compost suitable for a wide variety of plants. Can this be done ? The answer is a definite "yes". We have been able to show that almost all plants can be grown, not merely as well, but often better in the standard composts devised at the John Innes Institution. These composts are the outcome of a great many experiments but they are long past the experimental stage. Commercial, private and municipal growers are using them in increasing numbers and at the John Innes Institution large numbers of plants of widely different types, such as alpines, trees and shrubs, stove and greenhouse plants, ferns, bulbs, cacti, etc. have been for several years grown in these standard composts. Thus, where we have control of the factors governing the cultivation of plants under glass, scientific method can greatly assist the art of growing, though it will never entirely replace it.

There are other problems the gardener meets when preparing his composts. One is the increasing difficulty of procuring good leaf-mould or stable manure, particularly if his garden is situated near a large town. Yet organic material is an indispensable part of a compost, the physical condition and moisture holding capacities of which depend very largely upon it.

Although leaf-mould or stable manure may be used successfully in a compost, both materials possess certain undesirable qualities. No two samples are alike. The food value of both varies according to the composition, the manner of storing and the degree of decomposition. Now, where such variations exist in an essential ingredient of a compost it follows that crop results too, must vary. Uniformity of growth depends upon uniformity in the compost ingredients and the solution of this particular problem lies in finding a source of humus which will not vary in its composition, its nutritive value or its degree of decomposition.

Another problem is that of the increasing incidence of pests and diseases attacking seedlings and plants grown in pots. Since prevention is better than cure the sensible thing to do is to see that the soil at least is free from pests and diseases. Leaf-mould and animal manure usually contain organisms harmful to the growth of plants. Thus, these materials should not be used for raising seedlings or for growing pot plants, unless some means is employed for killing all the harmful organisms they contain. As an alternative a sterile source of humus could be used.

These and similar problems have not been overlooked and their solution has been considered in our attempts to rationalize the preparation and use of composts for pot plants.

It is probable that some of the materials and methods suggested in this book may seem unorthodox, perhaps even startling. We have tried, therefore, to present as simply as possible, a reasoned explanation for our recommendations. But no explanation can be entirely satisfactory unless it begins with the plant itself and explains what its foods are, what materials supply them, etc. Consequently we have dealt with these matters first, in order that the reader may better appreciate the principles underlying the methods advocated later in the book.

CHAPTER 2

THE PLANT'S FOOD

IN these days most of us know that the universe is built up of a limited number of raw materials, namely the 92 elements of the chemist. From combinations of various of these elementary building materials comes the immense variety of things, living and non-living, that we see around us. Some are simple compounds like water, which consists of two elements only, others such as plant and animal tissues are extremely complicated. All however can be resolved by suitable chemical methods into the elements composing them.

Thus analysis shows that the chief building materials which the plant takes from the air and soil around it are as follows. Nitrogen, phosphorus, sulphur, potassium, calcium and magnesium are used in considerable quantities ; iron, manganese, sodium, chlorine and silicon in smaller amounts, plus minute quantities of copper, zinc, boron, etc., the so-called trace elements. It is possible that some of these elements, e.g. chlorine and silicon are not essential, even though taken up by the plant. In addition plants utilize large amounts of hydrogen and oxygen in the form of water absorbed by the roots, and carbon is obtained by the leaves from the atmosphere.

Now these *nutritive elements*, as we shall call them, rarely occur in nature in a free state, but are combined with one another. Moreover, the plant cannot use them except in the form of compounds. For example, four-fifths of the air we and plants breathe consists of nitrogen, but this vast supply is not available to the plant, which takes up much of its nitrogen as nitrates (i.e. compounds of nitrogen and oxygen), and some as ammonia (a compound of nitrogen and hydrogen). Similarly phosphorus is taken in by the plant as phosphates, and potassium, calcium and magnesium as the salts of these metals. It is these chemical compounds absorbed by the plant which we shall refer to as "plant foods" and as we shall see later they are found in a variety of materials used by the gardener for "feeding" his plants. Before we pass on, however, we must look more closely into the relationship between the plant and its food supply.

With the exception of carbon, which is obtained by green leaves from the gas carbon-dioxide, always present in the atmosphere, the nutritive elements come from the soil, which under average conditions contains an abundant supply of plant food. Most of it, however, is unavailable to the plant, because plant food must be soluble in water before it can be utilized, and the bulk of the nutritive elements in the soil occur as insoluble compounds. By the action of chemical processes always going on in the soil the insoluble stores of plant food are very slowly converted into soluble or *available* food as it is called. Actually the proportion of water-soluble food present in the soil is very small indeed, but it is this small proportion which nourishes the plant.

Although the total amount of food absorbed by

the roots of a plant during its life may be very great, plants can only take up very weak nutrient solutions, and it is possible seriously to damage the plant by giving it food in too great a concentration. Some elements are capable of greater damage than others, for instance, if more than a trace of boron or copper is present growth may be weakened or even seriously damaged. Whether we should call such substances as boron a "food" is doubtful, nevertheless they are essential to the healthy growth of plants in the same way that vitamins are essential in animal nutrition. The absorption of soil water containing the dissolved nutrients is a finely balanced process, the amount of any particular element the plant can absorb depending on the amounts of the other elements available. Just as the builder cannot erect a house unless he has a sufficient supply of mortar as well as bricks, so each plant food has a definite place in the building up of the plant and each must be present in sufficient quantity if growth is to proceed normally. Thus there may be available in the soil an abundant supply of phosphate and potash, but if only very small amounts of available nitrogen are present then the other foods cannot be utilized. Further, the plant foods must not only be present in sufficient amount but also in the right proportions if the best growth is to be obtained. For example if too much calcium is present then the absorption of potassium and iron is retarded.

SOME SPECIALLY IMPORTANT FOODS.

Three of the nutritional elements, nitrogen, phosphorus and potassium are of special importance and for this reason we shall consider them in detail and note their general effects on the growing plant.

Nitrogen imparts a good green colour to leaves, encourages rapid growth, increases the size of leaves and stems and is in special demand when the plant is growing strongly. In excess it produces a rich dark green colour in the foliage, soft and sappy growth prone to fungoid diseases, delayed flowering and fruiting, reduced resistance to the effects of cold, and diminished quality in flowers, fruits and seeds. An excess in seed composts may prevent germination and retard seedling growth. Nitrogen deficiency in pot plants is shown by the yellowish-green colour of the foliage, especially along the veins; by the yellowing and shedding of the older leaves, together with a general decrease in the size of all parts of the plant.

Phosphorus is especially required for root (and leaf) growth in the seedling stages and for promoting seed and fruit development in the later stages of growth. It encourages early maturity and gives increased resistance to cold and disease. Phosphorus tends to counteract the effects of too much nitrogen. In excess it produces yellowish green foliage and hard growth in the early stages and unduly hastens maturity. A deficiency results in a general retardation of growth, a deep green colour in the seedling stage and increased susceptibility to variations in soil and climatic conditions.

Potassium is especially important in the building up in the plant of starches, sugars and fibrous tissues. It promotes sturdy growth of good green colour, improves the quality of fruits and increases the plant's resistance to disease, cold and drought. In excess, growth is checked and flower and seed production delayed. Deficiency of potassium results in stunted growth, mottling of the older leaves often developing into scorch, and increased susceptibility to damage from cold. Potassium and nitrogen are to a large extent complementary in their action, each apparently enabling the plant to make better use of the other food.

The other essential elements are almost always present in the soils used for making seed and potting composts though calcium (lime) is sometimes deficient. This element, besides being a necessary food, is important because it reduces soil acidity and increases the availability of other plant nutrients, especially phosphorus.

CHAPTER 3

NATURAL SOURCES OF PLANT FOOD

WE have seen that the plant foods are certain chemical compounds dissolved in the soil water and such being the case the shrewd gardener might very well ask "Is soil necessary; could not plants be grown in water to which these chemicals have been added?"

The answer is—soil is not necessary; and plants can be grown perfectly in a weak solution of chemicals. For many years research workers interested in growth problems have raised their plants in culture solutions made by adding chemicals to water. More recently, pronounced success has been achieved on a commercial scale using similar methods. The chemical compounds of nitrogen, phosphorus, etc. are the essential foods, and other things being equal, it does not matter to the plant whether it gets them from a culture solution, from the soil, from organic materials such as bones, or from chemical salts like superphosphate of lime. So long as a given nutritive element supplied by these materials is soluble in water, or becomes soluble, it is equally available and of equal value to the plant irrespective of its source. Let us put this in very plain words. *The plant feeds on chemical salts in solution*. We stress this point, since many gardeners fail to appreciate it and, for example, are prejudiced against inorganic fertilizers as plant foods, compared with organic fertilizers and animal manures. Though there may be all the difference in the world between the dry crystalline salt called sodium nitrate and squelchy cow manure, they act identically as regards the form of nitrogen they supply to the plant. The decision as to which may be the best to use in any given circumstances rests on other considerations such as the amount of food supplied, the cost and ease of use. Bearing this in mind, we may now turn to the materials used in composts as sources of plant food, and note their special characteristics.

The soil is one obvious source of plant food and artificial fertilizers another. In both cases we may consider the foods they supply under two headings; those derived from inorganic and those from organic materials.

THE SOIL

The inorganic or mineral part of soil consists of stones, sand, silt, clay and chalk together with air and water. The minerals are derived from the splitting up of rocks into fragments grading, without any break, from the coarsest particles (stones) through sand and silt to the finest particles (clay). Stones and sand supply no food whatever although they may be of value as drainage. Silt ranges in size from $\frac{1}{600}$th part of an inch down to $\frac{1}{12,000}$th part and constitutes a large proportion of the soil. Clay consists of microscopic particles of less than $\frac{1}{12,000}$th of an inch in diameter which, unlike fine sand and the coarser silts, react chemically with other inorganic constituents of the soil. Clay is a most important part of the soil, since it alone supplies certain of the mineral salts required by the plant. Clay particles therefore are essential in seed and potting composts. Chalk is visibly absent from many soils but there are few in which small quantities of calcium carbonate are not found. Air and water also are essential constituents of fertile soils, especially as they affect the numbers and activity of the beneficial bacteria, and together account for half or more of the bulk of the whole mass. Air is necessary for the proper functioning of the roots in their work of taking up the soil water without which plant life could no longer continue.

Stones, sand, silt, clay and chalk then are the chief mineral components of soil, and soils differ largely from one another because they consist of different proportions of these materials. Thus loams are mixtures of sand, silt and clay, light loams containing a greater proportion of sand than heavy loams, but less clay. Marls are loams containing chalk in addition to clay and sand. The yellow and red colour of some loams is due to the presence of varying amounts of oxide of iron.

The organic materials of the soil comprise plant and animal remains which, after being broken down by microscopic fungi and bacteria are gradually changed into a dark brown or black substance known as "humus". The decomposition or breaking down of plant and animal remains into successively simpler compounds is a very complex process, resulting finally in the production of nitrate, a form of nitrogen readily absorbed by plants.

Apart from its value as a source of nitrates, humus is of consequence in another way. We saw that flowering plants cannot utilize the free nitrogen of the atmosphere, but must always take up their nitrogen from the soil in combined form, e.g. as nitrate. Certain bacteria, however, can utilize atmospheric nitrogen directly, provided there is in the soil a proper supply of organic matter and chalk. When these bacteria die and are decomposed then the nitrogen they have absorbed becomes available to the plant as nitrates. Now nitrates are easily dissolved in rain water and liable to be washed out of the soil and there would ultimately be a serious shortage of this all important plant food were it not replaced through the agency of bacteria. Humus then is essential for the production of nitrate by the nitrifying bacteria and as a source of energy (i.e. food) for the nitrogen-fixing bacteria. Organic matter is indeed the only natural source of nitrogen for most plants, and as several kinds are used for making composts these will be dealt with separately.

STABLE MANURE

Dung or farmyard manure is not rich in plant foods, its chief value lying in the benefit it confers on soils as a good moisture-holding form of humus. An average sample contains about $\frac{1}{2}$ per cent. nitrogen, $\frac{1}{4}$ per cent. phosphoric acid and $\frac{1}{2}$ per cent potash, some of each nutrient being slow and some quick acting. When well rotted it may contain double these amounts if it has been protected from rain and has been well compacted. Cow manure differs but little from horse manure in its food value and both vary greatly in quality according to the feeding of the animals, the method of storing and the age of the manure. Stable manure often contains many weed seeds, worms, etc.

PEAT

Peat is usually found in regions with a humid temperate climate where the land is swampy. The plants found in such localities are the moisture-loving types such as sphagnum mosses, sedges and cotton grass. As the plants, or their parts, die and fall they are covered by the surface water which largely excludes air and the bacteria responsible for the processes of decay. Because of this and owing also to the action of organic acids present, complete decay of the plant remains is prevented and "peat" is formed. If these conditions persist they lead to the gradual accumulation of peat, and with the passage of time deposits many feet thick may be formed. The nature of the peat (its texture, chemical composition, acidity, etc.) will depend mainly on the type of vegetation from which it is formed ; and this in turn will vary with the changes in the climate, drainage and soil conditions. Thus peat deposits may show different layers derived from different sorts of plants. These layers sometimes include roots of trees and shrubs and mineral soil. Peat also varies in character with the depth at which it is found. Near the surface it is brown, fibrous, light and porous ; lower down it tends to be black, heavy and dense, the blacker peat being the more decomposed.

In addition to this, peat has another valuable property, that of holding moisture. Peat can hold as much as from 90 to 95 per cent. of water, or over a dozen times its own weight, and even when it is apparently bone dry, water may comprise 30 per cent. of the whole. By comparison, the average loam holds about half its own dry weight of water. On light and porous soils the value of this property is obvious: water, instead of filtering down to levels beyond the reach of the plant, is held by the peat, to be drawn upon by the plant's roots as required. Peat, if decomposed, also helps to bind light soils and give them body.

Compared with that of the average garden soil the nutrient value of peat is very low. The quantity of nitrogen usually present is about one per cent., but only a small amount of this is available at a time. Phosphate, potash and calcium are usually also deficient, and where peat is used in quantity all three nutrients should be added to make good the natural shortage.

Although the nutrient value of peat is low, nevertheless because of its high organic content it plays a most important part in improving and maintaining the fertility of composts. Very few of the beneficial bacteria which form an essential link in plant nutrition are found in peat as it naturally occurs. As it rots, however, it is changed into humus upon which the bacteria thrive and upon which soil fertility depends.

LEAF-MOULD

Leaf-mould, when pure and of the right kind, is an excellent source of humus. However, as collected or sold it not infrequently contains a certain amount of soil and sand, and the humus content is then proportionately less. It also varies greatly in quality, depending on (1) the manner and degree of decomposition (2) the kind of leaves from which it is made. In regard to decomposition, leaves which decompose in a thin layer on the woodland floor seem to make a much better mould than those rotted in a heap in the garden. To obtain equal results artificially, the moist leaves should be gathered into a heap and composted with the aid of a little sulphate of ammonia and lime, as with vegetable refuse. The degree of decomposition is important since unless the material is thoroughly rotted adverse, even toxic, effects on plant growth will ensue. As regards the kind of leaves used, oak and beach are traditionally held to be superior to all others for pot plants. For use in composts leaf-mould should be moist and well rotted so that it readily crumbles into small brownish-black flakes. Its manurial value is not high, the nitrogen content rarely exceeding 1 per cent. In comparison with the moss and sedge peats the amount of available nitrogen is slightly greater and the total phosphate and potash contents are also higher.

CHAPTER 4

ARTIFICIAL SOURCES OF PLANT FOOD

FOREMOST among these materials are the "fertilizers". By fertilizers we mean those materials, other than soil and stable manure, commonly used as sources of plant food. We shall only refer to those fertilizers which are most likely to be of use in the growing of pot plants. As we have seen, some plant foods are present in the soil in sufficient quantities for plant requirements. On the other hand nitrogen, phosphorus and potassium, which may be described as the three elements of fertility, are rarely present in quantities sufficient to ensure a full crop. Consequently they are the elements supplied in fertilizer mixtures.

Some fertilizers supply one plant food only, others two or three. It is convenient to refer to mixtures containing nitrogen, phosphorus and potassium as *complete* fertilizers; to mixtures of two nutrients as *compound* fertilizers and to those which supply one food only as *single* fertilizers.

Before the gardener can make the best use of fertilizers there is one thing he should take pains to understand and that is how to compare fertilizers for their food values. Before buying a fertilizer, he should always ask for the "analysis". This tells him which food or foods the fertilizer supplies and the amount. This amount is always expressed as a percentage of the total weight of the material. Thus, if the analysis of sulphate of ammonia reads "20 per cent. nitrogen," it means that one fifth of the whole is nitrogen, i.e. in a 5 lb. bag there is 1 lb. of nitrogen. Not infrequently, the analysis for nitrogenous fertilizers is given in terms of ammonia, as well as, or instead of nitrogen. This practice is both unnecessary and confusing. The nitrogen analysis is sufficient and should be made the standard.

In the case of the phosphatic fertilizers it is customary to refer, not to the percentage of phosphorus, but to the percentage of phosphoric acid, indicated by the chemical symbols P_2O_5. Further, the phosphoric acid may be in a water-soluble or insoluble form so that the analysis may read "so much" water soluble and "so much" insoluble phosphoric acid. The soluble phosphoric acid is at once available to the plant. The insoluble phosphoric acid on contact with the moist soil is changed to a soluble form, a little at a time, and so becomes available. As in the case of the nitrogenous fertilizers the analysis of phosphatic fertilizers may be given in two different ways, as the percentage of phosphoric acid or as the percentage of calcium phosphate. It would be better to drop the latter, which is misleading, and to compare phosphatic fertilizers in terms of soluble and insoluble phosphoric acid.

Potassic fertilizers are compared on the percentage of potash (K_2O) they contain; and lime, chalk, etc., on the percentage of calcium oxide (CaO).

ORGANIC NITROGENOUS FERTILIZERS

Hoof and Horn meal or grist is a single fertilizer made by grinding up the hoofs and horns of cattle. The finer the grinding, the greater is the amount of available nitrogen. Hoof is richer in nitrogen than horn, so the percentage of nitrogen varies with the proportion of horn. A good hoof and horn grist should contain about 13 per cent. nitrogen. Hoof and horn, like all organic fertilizers, has to be decomposed by bacterial action before it yields the nitrates the plant can assimilate, but even so, some of it is soon available. Under correct soil conditions this fertilizer is much quicker acting than is commonly supposed.

Dried Blood is sold as a nitrogenous fertilizer, though it also contains calcium, sodium, potassic and phosphatic compounds. It generally contains 12 to 14 per cent. of nitrogen and is a quick acting fertilizer.

INORGANIC NITROGENOUS FERTILIZERS

Ammonium sulphate (sulphate of ammonia) is a single fertilizer, an increasing quantity of which is now being made by synthetic processes. It is also a by-product from gas works and coke-oven plants. Sulphate of ammonia contains about 21 per cent. of nitrogen in the form of ammonia and is rapid in action. It is soluble in water and to a slight extent may be washed out of the soil by watering.

Sodium nitrate (nitrate of soda) is a single fertilizer made synthetically from the nitrogen of the atmosphere. It contains about 16 per cent. nitrogen in the nitrate form, is soluble in water and slightly quicker in effect than sulphate of ammonia. It is liable to be washed out of the soil by watering.

Ammonium nitrate is a single fertilizer containing about 34 per cent. of nitrogen, half as ammonia and half as nitrate. It is the most concentrated of all the inorganic nitrogenous fertilizers. It contains nothing but plant food and is an ideal source of nitrogen for the plant. It must be kept in air-tight containers, however, since it greedily absorbs moisture. It is soluble in water and the most rapid in action of the nitrogenous fertilizers.

ORGANIC PHOSPHATIC FERTILIZERS

Bone meal is prepared by removing the fat (but not the gelatin) from bones and grinding them to a fine meal. It is a slow acting compound fertilizer containing about 22 per cent. of insoluble phosphoric acid and 4 per cent. of nitrogen (from the gelatin).

Steamed Bone Flour differs from bone meal in that the gelatin and other nitrogenous constituents are removed in addition to the fat. The nitrogen content is about 1 per cent. and the insoluble phosphoric acid from 25 to 30 per cent. It is a slow acting compound fertilizer, very similar to bone meal in most respects.

INORGANIC PHOSPHATIC FERTILIZERS

Superphosphate is made by treating finely ground rock phosphates with sulphuric acid to convert them to a form soluble in water. It contains 14 to 18 per cent. of phosphoric acid and is a quick acting single fert.lizer. Although the phosphoric acid in superphosphate is soluble in water it is not washed from a compost by watering, since when mixed with soil, it is converted into a less soluble form which is still in the main available to plants. Superphosphate besides being rapid in action lasts a long time and is an ideal phosphatic fertilizer.

Basic slag is a by-product from steel furnaces. It is a compound fertilizer containing from 10 to 18 per

cent. of insoluble phosphoric acid, together with certain
calcium compounds. The value of basic slag depends
directly upon the fineness of grinding. It is a slow acting
fertilizer.

Inorganic Potassic Fertilizer

Sulphate of potash is the only potassic fertilizer that
is safe to use in potting composts. Potash is present in
large quantities in rock deposits in Germany and France.
Sulphate of potash is a single fertilizer prepared from the
crude rock salts and contains 48 per cent. of pure
potash (K_2O). It is a quick acting fertilizer, soluble in
water, but is not readily washed out from the soil.

Organic Potassic Fertilizer

Wood Ash when fresh may contain 5 to 15 per cent. of
pure potash along with calcium and other foods. The
potash is readily soluble in water.

Lime (Calcium Oxide)

There are three forms of lime used in gardens, the
oxide, the hydroxide and the carbonate.

Calcium oxide, the most concentrated form of lime,
is known as quicklime or burnt lime and is obtained by
burning limestone or chalk in kilns. It may be purchased
as lump lime or, when ground to a fine powder, as
ground lime. Mixed with the soil or exposed to the air
it quickly absorbs moisture and is then changed to the
hydroxide form, known as slaked lime. Quicklime is
caustic in action and not to be recommended for pot
plants.

Calcium hydroxide, known also as hydrated or slaked

lime, has no scorching action on plants and has the advantage of uniformity and fineness of division.

Calcium carbonate is the form of lime occurring naturally in limestone and chalk, which differ only in their hardness and compactness. Limestone is usually ground to a fine powder and is a very convenient form of lime for potting composts. A very pure chalk can sometimes be procured as a by-product from water works at little cost other than that of cartage.

Mortar rubble has for many years been incorporated by gardeners in their composts for the dual purpose of supplying lime and drainage. The average amount of lime in mortar rubble is about 20 per cent. It is extremely variable, depending largely on the amount of plaster (which is useless as a source of lime) and brick present. It is an unreliable material, especially now various proprietary plasters are being used in the building trade. Cases have been reported where substances dangerous to plants have been introduced by mortar rubble.

CHAPTER 5

COMPOST MATERIALS

WHAT are the qualities of a good compost? Clearly we are not in a position to decide what materials are to be used unless we first know what our standard of quality is to be. How can we define the essential requirements of a compost of the highest quality? Our definition is given below. We believe it is the first time that such a definition has been given. It may interest growers to make a critical comparison between these standards and those which have satisfied them hitherto.

The essential characteristics of a good compost are as follows :

1. *It should be in good physical condition, i.e. it should possess a crumby structure that permits the entry of air and be able to hold sufficient moisture while permitting excess to drain away.*
2. *It should provide an adequate and balanced food supply for the plant at every stage of its growth.*
3. *It should be free from all harmful organisms and substances.*

The quality of the plants is of paramount importance, whether it be from the point of view of the commercial grower who has to sell his plants in order to make a living, or that of the public or private gardener who has to satisfy his employer in order to keep his job. For both men, composts must be consistently good and reliable, so that the risk of failure is eliminated so far as the soil is concerned and certainty of success thereby assured. But this is not all. The cost of labour and materials must be kept as low as possible and methods of working must be simple and easy. Finally if a compost is to be universally acceptable in these days, it should dispense with stable manure which is increasingly difficult to obtain, especially in or near large towns where so many people have to do their gardening.

Thus to our three primary requirements for an ideal compost we add six others :

4. *The materials must be easy to get.*
5. *They must be reasonably cheap.*
6. *They must be uniform in quality.*
7. *Each material should as far as possible be chosen for one purpose only.*
8. *Animal manure must be excluded.*
9. *The method of composting must be simple.*

The reason for 7 needs further explanation. Consistency in results demands that the gardener should be able to make up exactly the same compost each time. This he cannot do unless he is able to control independently each ingredient of the compost. Thus the chief purpose of including organic matter is to bring the compost to the correct physical condition ; it is not desirable that it should also supply unknown amounts of plant food, as do some forms of organic matter, since nutrients can be added independently. Similarly, basic slag is not the best phosphatic fertilizer to use in a compost because it introduces an unknown quantity of lime. It is much better to add separately known quantities of phosphate and lime.

If the nine principles set out above are fulfilled, then by simplification and standardization the growing of pot plants is made an easier, cheaper and more certain business, and science becomes the handmaiden of art in the potting shed. In the remaining pages of this chapter we propose to examine more closely the compost materials we recommend.

LOAM

By loam we mean a soil in which the proportions of sand, silt and clay are nicely balanced and containing usually from 2 to 7 per cent. of humus. Medium loams contain just enough clay to be slightly greasy when smeared, without being sticky. Light loams contain more sand, heavy loams more clay than medium loams. Light, heavy and chalky loams should not be used for composts. Suitable loam is slightly on the acid side (pH 6·5 to 5·5). Loams are obtained either from arable or pasture land, the first being arable loam and the second turf or garden loam.

Loam is the main ingredient of seed and potting composts, to which it gives "body". Its chief function is to supply the clay and actively decomposing humus which are so essential for good plant growth.

Turf loam is the product obtained when turves, cut from a pasture on a loam soil, are stacked in a heap until the grass and some of the roots have rotted. The best material comes from a good pasture and consists of the top 4–5 inches of turf and soil cut into turves about 12 by 9 inches. A good pasture is one which has been properly drained, and has had sufficient lime, manure (by grazing) or fertilizers to encourage a thick sward of fine grasses. *The loam which will grow good pot plants is the one which has grown good grasses.*

Where turf loam is not available, loamy soil from arable land may be used. The most suitable arable soils are deep fertile loams " in good heart."

Loam for use in potting composts requires standardizing in three respects : namely, its clay and humus contents, and *p*H value.

The clay content is standardized by choosing a medium loam which is slightly greasy when smeared, without being sticky. The humus content is standardized by choosing a turf loam. The calcium content should be standardized in the stack by adding ground chalk or limestone, on the recommendation of the Advisory Officer, to bring up the *p*H to 6·3. The chalk should be added to every 9 inch depth of turves. If an inferior loam has to be used, it may be improved by adding a 2 inch layer of horse manure, alternating with the chalk.

Turves should be cut when the grass is thick, in April—May, and stacked with slight gaps for aeration. *The turves should never be stacked in dry condition*, and the hosepipe should be used to saturate them if necessary. The stack will then be ready for use in about six months time.

Loam which is to be sterilized in bins should be dry. This can be achieved quite easily by proper handling of the stack. If the loam is thoroughly moist when stacked the turves will rot down fairly quickly. Then, a month or two before the loam is wanted for use, all that remains to be done is to keep rain off the stack by covering it with corrugated iron. The stack will then

dry out of its own accord. The grower will soon learn
from experience precisely when the stack should be
covered. When chopping down the stack, a spade
should be used and thin cuts made *from top to bottom*
across the full breadth of the stack. By so doing, the
effects of variations in the quality of the turves are
minimized and intimate mixing ensured.

Humus

As we saw in the last chapter there are three sources
of humus commonly available for use in seed and potting
composts, namely leaf-mould, rhododendron-peat and
moss- and sedge-peats.

Leaf-mould, which is practically all humus when
rotted, varies greatly in quality according to the leaves
from which it is made and its age. It usually contains
weed seeds, worms, etc., and may introduce diseases.
For these reasons, peat is to be preferred.

The value of peat in a compost is as a soil "conditioner." Its spongy nature makes its unique: it can
aerate a compost and regulate its moisture-holding
qualities at one and the same time. And for a long
time, since it decomposes slowly. It has the merits of
being (i) naturally highly sterile and free from weed
seeds, pests and diseases, (ii) highly uniform in texture
and varying only a little in quality. This uniformity is
a great asset to the grower who wishes to make up
standard composts.

Peat suitable for composts is sold either in compressed bales or loose, and is variously described as
moss peat, sedge peat, granulated peat, etc. In choosing
a peat the most important factor is texture. The peat

should be of a fibrous or granulated type, relatively undecomposed and not dusty or apt to powder when handled. The particles should grade fairly evenly up to $\frac{3}{8}$ inch in size, with a preponderance of $\frac{1}{8}$ inch particles. The pH should not be less than 3·5. Dusty, fine peats should be strictly avoided, also black, greasy, decomposed ones. "Rhododendron" peat, which contains bracken roots, together with silt and sand, should not be used. Peat, whether purchased loose or in bales, should be kept dry and clean under cover, where weeds and weed seeds cannot contaminate it.

In their effect on physical condition the peats are definitely superior to leaf-mould, which soon rots away and has much poorer moisture holding capacity. This is another reason why we select peat as the best source of humus for composts. Should it not be easy to obtain, then good leaf-mould may be used instead, especially if it can be had merely for the labour of collecting it.

SAND

Sand must be added to seed and potting composts to obtain correct physical condition and good drainage. It should be clean and sharp, and free from clay, silt, lime (e.g. shells) and organic matter and should grade evenly from fine to coarse particles. Few of the horticultural sands in England are as coarse as could be desired.

Loam, peat and sand then constitute the basis of good composting. The only other materials which need be used are four fertilizers, but before dealing with these we must consider the all important matter of physical condition.

CHAPTER 6

THE COMPOST : PHYSICAL CONDITION.

THE first of the three prime requirements for a good compost is that it should be in correct physical or mechanical condition, i.e. well aerated, of good texture, having good moisture holding capacities and draining freely.

Most loams, especially the medium and heavier ones, are too close in texture and too cold when used alone for seed sowing, or pot work. There is not enough air in them, their moisture holding capacity is bad, they become wet and sticky after watering and are apt to dry out too rapidly, leaving a hard and cracked surface. These rapid fluctuations from wet to dry are especially harmful to seedlings and may damage even large plants. In addition more attention to watering is needed and labour thereby increased. The loam may be improved by the addition of sand but only the addition of organic matter can produce a compost that really handles nicely or is in the right physical condition. We have already seen that good peat is the best source of humus for seed and potting composts. A fibrous or granular, relatively undecomposed peat will not break down too rapidly in the soil. Owing to its spongy nature it holds apart the particles of loam, preventing them from forming a sticky mass, i.e. peat breaks up loam and makes it more friable, and caking and panning are prevented.

The mixing of loam, peat and sand in the right

proportions is of vital importance to many plants, and bad germination, poor growth and damping off are

Fig. 1. *Streptocarpus* seedlings. Comparison of the two pans on the left shows the importance of physical condition in a compost. Comparison of the two pans at the bottom shows the effect of phosphate in helping the seedling to overcome bad physical condition

often the result of neglect in this particular. Seeds vary to a great extent in their ability to germinate in badly made composts. Large seeds (e.g. tomato) usually have sufficient energy to enable germination and a limited amount of growth to take place whatever compost is used. With smaller seeds (e.g. *Begonia*), greater care is necessary and unless the physical condition of the compost is correct, both germination and seedling growth will suffer (Fig. 1).

In the past it has been customary for gardeners in preparing composts to vary the proportions of loam, humus and sand to "suit" the particular plants to be raised. Numerous comparisons that we have made show that this practice is quite unnecessary, *so long as a proper supply of food is available*. At the most two composts are sufficient, and for a great many plants one will do.

Using medium loam containing little or no visible sand a compost will be in correct physical condition when the ingredients are in the following proportions.

Seed Compost :
    2 parts by bulk medium loam
    1 ,, ,, ,, peat (or leaf-mould)
    1 ,, ,, ,, coarse sand
Potting compost :
    7 parts by bulk medium loam
    3 ,, ,, ,, peat (or leaf-mould)
    2 ,, ,, ,, coarse sand

The proportions for a potting compost may need modifying, according to the nature of the loam. Light loams contain more sand than medium loams, therefore a smaller amount need be added. For example using a light loam the proportions could be 8 *parts loam*, $2\frac{1}{2}$ *parts organic matter and* $1\frac{1}{2}$ *parts coarse sand.* If coarse sand cannot be procured, then the proportion of sand must be increased a little. In many cases the proportions of loam, peat and sand as recommended for a potting compost can be adopted for seed sowing, also, thus further simplifying compost requirements.

For strong growing plants like chrysanthemums and tomatoes and for crowded boxes, the last mentioned proportions might be used to advantage even with a medium loam. Whatever the proportions the gardener decides upon they should apply to all the plants grown. We repeat, there is no need whatever to have a number of composts. Two are ample for the overwhelming majority of plants and once the proportions of the ingredients have been adjusted according to the nature of the loam they should be adhered to.

So much for the proportions of loam, peat and sand required to ensure that the compost is in good physical condition. Do these ingredients at the same time provide a proper supply of food ? We must now proceed to examine this matter.

CHAPTER 7

THE COMPOST: FOOD SUPPLY

THE second of the three prime requirements for a good compost is that it should contain an adequate and balanced food supply at every stage of the plant's life. It is an almost universal practice for plants to be fed with liquid or other fertilizers as they become pot bound and approach maturity, therefore most adult plants receive a fairly good supply of food (though it may not always be balanced). But during the period between germination and pricking off, the plant is often undernourished, though most gardeners are quite unaware of this, with the result that growth is often delayed and germination sometimes affected.

Gardeners and gardening text books have for years stated that no manure or fertilizers should be added to seed composts. No one seems to have challenged this statement, with the result that few people know what great improvements can be made in the quality of seedling growth simply by adding fertilizers to the seed compost. (Let it be said at once that experiments on a variety of plants as different from one another as gooseberries and gherkins have demonstrated beyond doubt the truth of this statement.) How did the fallacy arise that fertilizers (and manures) should not be added to seed composts? Probably for two reasons, first because far too large quantities were used, and secondly,

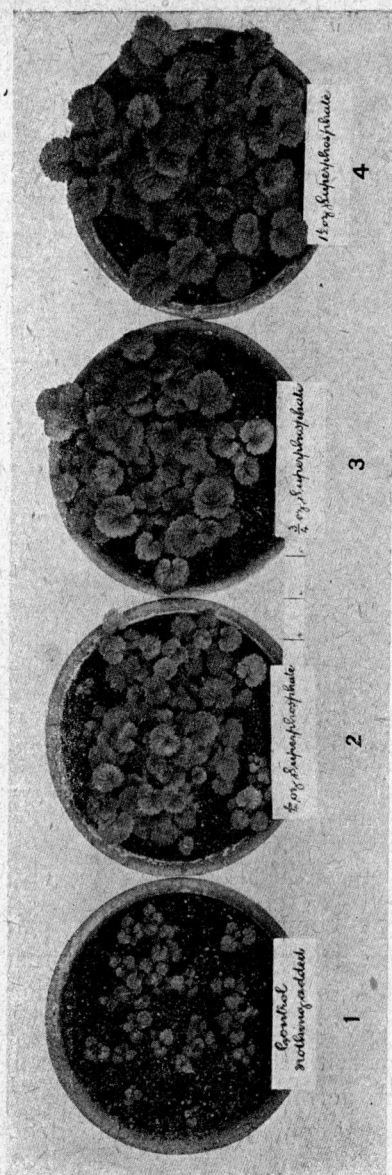

Fig. 2.—*Primula malacoides.* Showing the effect of adding increasing amounts of superphosphate to a seed compost

1. nothing added
2. $\frac{1}{4}$ oz. superphosphate added ⎫
3. $\frac{3}{4}$ oz.   ,,   ,, ⎬ per bushel of soil
4. $1\frac{1}{2}$ oz.   ,,   ,, ⎭

because they were the wrong kind or were in the wrong proportions.

Now the most critical stages of the plant's life begin with germination and include the early weeks up to the time of the first potting. Undernourishment at this period lays the plant open to the attack of diseases, and damage from many cultural conditions when it can least resist them. No amount of feeding in the later

Fig. 3. *Tomato*. Most British loams are deficient in phosphate and many in lime
Left :   loam, nothing added
Middle :   loam, phosphate added
Right :   loam, phosphate and chalk added

stages of growth can compensate for underfeeding the seedling plant, hence it is vitally important that there should be an ample supply of food in the seedling stages. There should be no check to the maximum rate of growth, consistent with sturdiness, from the moment the seed begins to germinate.

Why is it that seed composts are usually deficient in

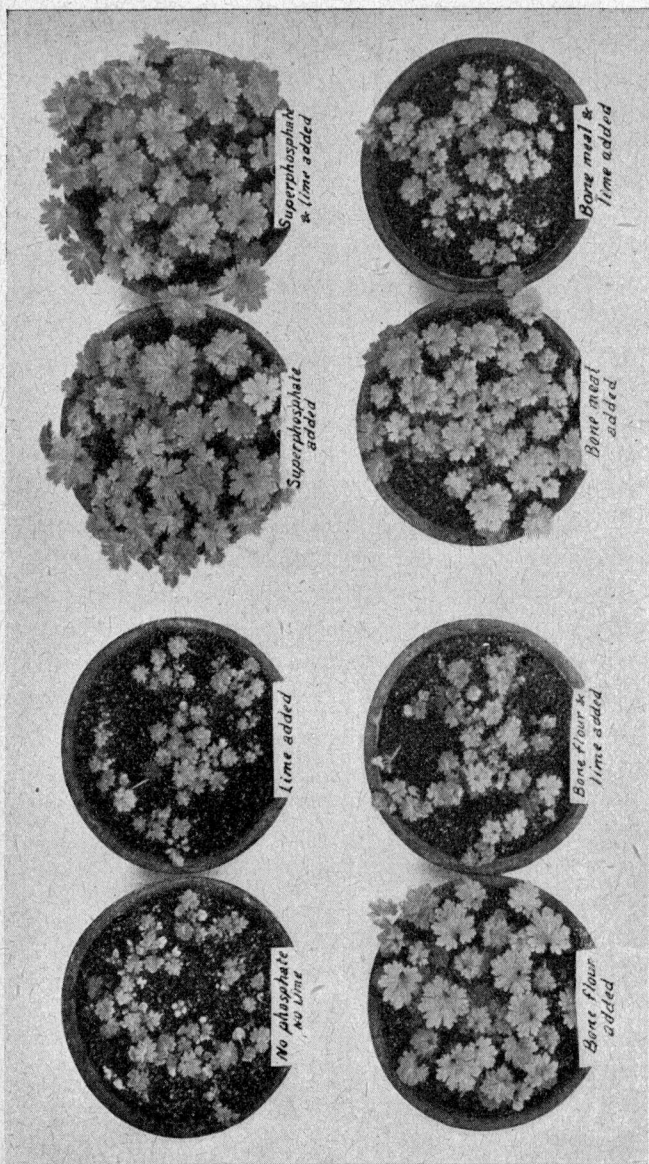

Fig. 4.—*Primula sinensis*. Showing the effect of adding three different phosphatic fertilizers to a seed compost, with and without lime (calcium carbonate). Note the favourable superphosphate-lime and unfavourable bone-lime reactions

plant food? The answer is that loam, which is the chief source of plant food in seed composts, is usually deficient in available phosphate (Fig. 2). Now we saw in Chapter 2 that phosphate is especially important in the early stages of seedling growth. Numerous experiments have shown that poor growth due to phosphate deficiency is seen before the pricking out stage is reached, therefore it is imperative that phosphate be added to the compost *before* seed sowing. The best form of phosphate to make good this deficiency is superphosphate. Superphosphate is chosen because, first it is the only single fertilizer supplying water-soluble phosphoric acid, secondly it is quick acting and thirdly it is effective in supplying phosphoric acid over a long period.

Our experiments have shown that many loams are also deficient in calcium which must be added to get the best results not only to make good the deficiency but because superphosphate is most effective in a compost when a little calcium carbonate is also added (Fig. 3), It is not generally understood that the bone fertilizers do not react favourably in the presence of lime (Fig. 4). Ground limestone or chalk is chosen for supplying calcium since, for seedlings, these materials are safer to use than quicklime or hydrated lime. It is probably best not to add lime to a compost if the loam is neutral (*p*H 7·0) or alkaline.

The increase in vigour, rate of growth and the general health of young seedlings following the addition of small amounts of superphosphate and calcium carbonate to the seed compost is very definite and often astonishingly great (Fig. 5). Plants differ in

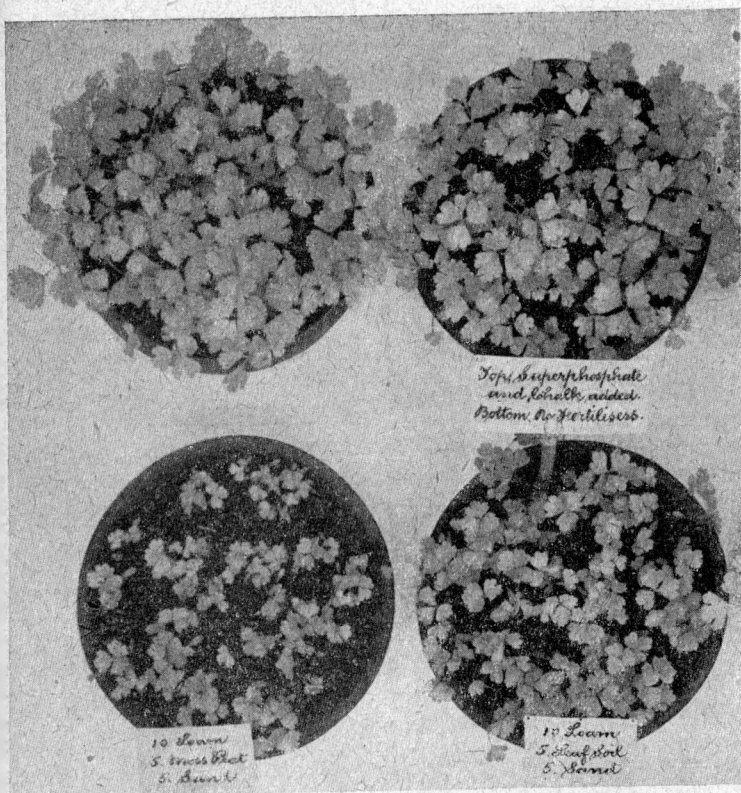

Fig. 5.—Celery.

      Left : 2 parts loam, 1 peat, 1 sand
      Right : 2 parts loam, 1 leaf-mould, 1 sand
      Bottom : no fertilizers added
      Top : superphosphate and chalk added

Comparison of the two lower pans shows slightly better growth in the leaf-mould mixture, due to its higher nutrient value. This difference is completely eliminated (two upper pans) when phosphate and chalk are added to the composts and a great improvement in growth is obtained

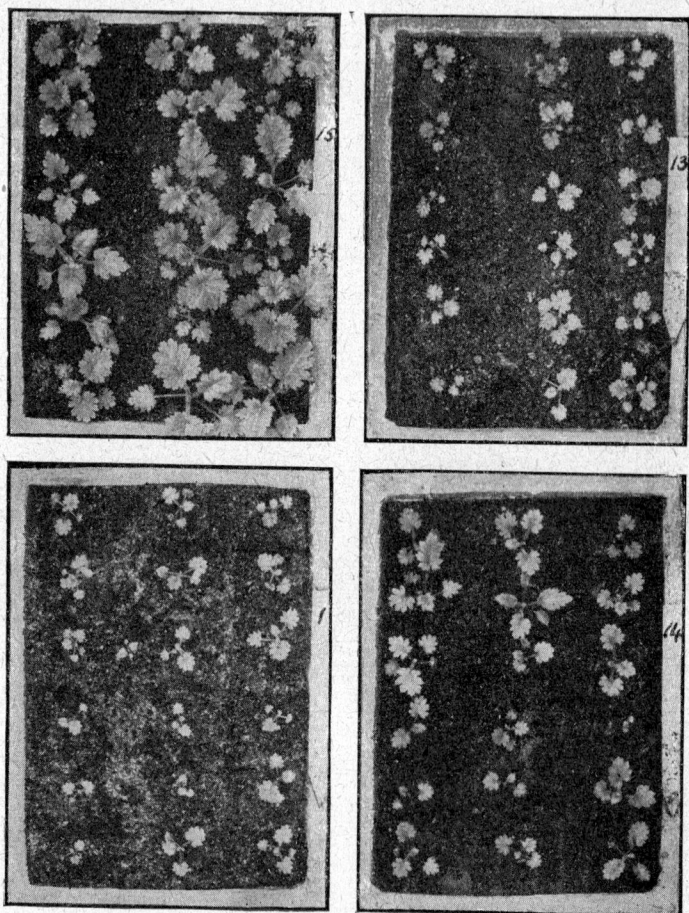

Fig. 6.—*Primula sinensis.* Showing the effect of adding single fertilizers to a seed
compost

Left : top, phosphate added   Right : top, potash added
Left : bottom, nothing added   Right : bottom, nitrogen added

In almost all seed composts there is enough nitrogen and potash for seedling
requirements, but not enough phosphate

their response to these fertilizers. For example at one extreme is *Primula malacoides* which visibly responds to addition of phosphate within a week, while at the other extreme are the big-seeded plants like peas with a large store of food within the seed, which may not show any improvement for 3 or 4 weeks. The majority of plants, however, reveal a marked improvement within two weeks of germination, that is *before* they are ready for pricking off. Foods other than phosphate and calcium carbonate are almost always present in loam in ample amounts for *seedling* requirements (Fig. 6) and need not be added.

By the time the average seedling is large enough to transfer to a $3\frac{1}{2}$ inch pot it is beginning to need more nitrogen and potash than is present in a seed compost, and our experiments have shown that if there is to be no check to growth these foods must be added so that they are available immediately they are required. For pot plants we need a source of nitrogen which will *immediately and continuously* supply the plant's requirements. Hoof and horn grist has proved to be the best nitrogenous fertilizer in these respects. Similarly sulphate of potash is chosen because it is the purest of the single potash fertilizers and because it is quick acting and long lasting.

We see therefore that both seed and potting composts must have fertilizers added to them if the plant's food supply is to be adequate and balanced. The amounts and other details regarding the use of these fertilizers are given in the chapter which follows.

CHAPTER 8

THE JOHN INNES COMPOSTS

WE now see that to get consistently good results the compost ingredients—loam, peat and sand—must be in certain proportions (for texture) and have fertilizers added (for nutrition). The third requirement, necessary to gain full advantage from the other two, is that the loam should be sterilized. This process is fully described in Chapters 9 and 10. In what follows, "sterilized" should be read before "loam". But where the grower is unable to sterilize, good unsterilized loam mixed as described should give results superior to ordinary rule-of-thumb practice, if not so good as those obtained from using the complete John Innes system. One warning must be given: the balance of fertilizers, which is correct for steam sterilized loam, may not give an equally good nutritional balance with unsterilized material.

INGREDIENTS OF THE COMPOSTS

John Innes Seed Compost

Parts by bu k $\begin{cases} \text{2 Loam} \\ \text{1 Peat} \\ \text{1 Sand} \end{cases}$ + $\begin{cases} \text{Super } 1\frac{1}{2} \text{ ozs.} \\ \text{Chalk } \frac{3}{4} \text{ oz.} \end{cases}$ per bushel

or

$\begin{cases} \text{Super 2 lbs.} \\ \text{Chalk 1 lb.} \end{cases}$ per cubic yard

John Innes Potting Compost

Parts by bulk $\begin{cases} 7 \text{ Loam} \\ 3 \text{ Peat} \\ 2 \text{ Sand} \end{cases}$ + $\begin{cases} \text{J.I. Base } \frac{1}{4} \text{ lb.} \\ \text{Chalk } \frac{3}{4} \text{ oz.} \end{cases}$ *per bushel*

or

$\begin{cases} \text{J.I. Base } 5 \text{ lbs.} \\ \text{Chalk } 1 \text{ lb.} \end{cases}$ *per cubic yard*

Super=superphosphate of lime, 18% phosphoric acid.
Chalk=ground chalk, ground limestone, limestone flour or whiting.

The *John Innes Base* can be bought from various sundriesmen. Its formula is:

Parts by Weight $\begin{cases} 2 \text{ Hoof and horn, } \frac{1}{8} \text{ inch grist (13\% nitrogen).} \\ 2 \text{ Superphosphate of lime (18\% phosphoric acid).} \\ 1 \text{ Sulphate of potash (48\% pure potash).} \end{cases}$

Approx. analysis: nitrogen 5.1%, phosphoric acid 7.2%, potash 9.7%.

In the compost formulæ the proportions of loam, peat and sand are correct for a medium loam. For lighter loams they may need modifying, as explained on p. 48.

The chalk is an essential ingredient in the composts and should always be added except in the case of some calcifuge plants. For example, *Erica gracilis* and *Rhododendron racemosum* do very well in the standard compost, whereas for *Rhododendron ambiguum* and *Gentiana Farreri* it is better to omit the chalk. Readers who wish to grow calcifuge plants in the J.I. composts should try some with and some without chalk and note for themselves which mixture gives the best results.

The figures given for the fertilizers are the outcome of numerous experiments and gardeners should not try to vary the proportions on their own account. The amounts should be strictly adhered to and not merely approximated; the weighing should be entrusted to someone who can be thoroughly relied upon. It is surprising to find how many gardeners will not invest a trifling sum in a pair of scales, but imagine that a potful of this or a teaspoonful of that represent accurate measurements. Guesswork should not be employed, either for measuring the fertilizers or the soil. It is quite easy to construct a measure* or to use a wheelbarrow of known capacity.

PREPARING THE COMPOSTS

The loam and peat need preparing before mixing, as follows. See that the loam is in good friable condition and if necessary spread it out to dry. Sift it through a $\frac{3}{8}$ inch sieve. If the peat is from a compressed bale break it up by rubbing through a $\frac{3}{8}$ inch sieve. Peat as purchased in bales or bags is usually very dry and must be sprinkled *lightly* with a fine rose-can. The reason the loam and peat are riddled through a $\frac{3}{8}$ inch sieve is that both seed and potting composts are wanted free from lumps, as these if left will be devoid of fertilizers and poorer than the surrounding soil. Our aim should be to have every thimbleful of compost rich in fertilizers and of good texture.

* See page 79.

Care should be taken throughout to ensure thorough mixing. The best way to accomplish this is to spread out the loam a few inches deep (not in a conical heap) on the mixing floor, the peat similarly on top of the the loam and the sand last. The sand should be dry so that it runs easily. Part of it is kept back and to this the fertilizers are added and thoroughly mixed. The fertilized sand is then distributed as evenly as possible over the rest of the soil, which is then cut down and turned over 3 or 4 times in the usual way.

Time will be saved if sufficient compost is made to last for several weeks. It should not, however, be kept for more than two months or it may become too acid for some plants.

As the two composts are difficult to distinguish from one another it is best to add 1 part in 36 (by bulk) of $\frac{1}{8}$ to $\frac{1}{4}$ inch red brick rubble to the potting compost, then if the two composts happen to be on the bench at the same time they will not be confused. *They should never be mixed together.*

USING THE COMPOSTS

Under average conditions the seed compost is used for seed sowing and pricking off and the potting compost for potting into $3\frac{1}{2}$ inch or larger pots. The species, the vigour of the plant and the time of the year, however, may necessitate modification. The best compost to be used for the successive stages of growth has been worked out for a number of plants.

BEST COMPOST SEQUENCE

Variety	Sowing	Boxes	60's	48's
Asparagus Fern	J.I.S.	—	J.I.P.1	J.I.P.2
Bedding Plants	J.I.S.	J.I.P.2	—	—
Carnation (rooted cuttings)	—	—	J.I.P.2	—
Cauliflower (January sown)	J.I.S.	—	J.I.P.3	—
Chrysanthemum (rooted cuttings)	—	—	J.I.P.1	J.I.P.2— J.I.P.3*
Cineraria	J.I.P.1	—	J.I.P.2	J.I.P.2
Cucumber	J.I.P.1	—	J.I.P.2	J.I.P.3
Cyclamen	J.I.S.	J.I.S.	J.I.S.	J.I.P.1
Lettuce (winter)	J.I.S.	J.I.P.2	—	—
Lettuce (spring)	J.I.S.	J.I.P.3	—	—
Primula malacoides	J.I.S.	—	J.I.P.1	J.I.P.2
Primula obconica	J.I.S.	—	J.I.P.1	J.I.P.2
Primula sinensis	J.I.S.	—	J.I.P.1	J.I.P.2
Solanum capsicastrum	J.I.P.1	—	J.I.P.2	J.I.P.2
Strawberry	—	—	J.I.P.1	J.I.P.3
Tomato (winter)	J.I.S.	—	J.I.P.1	—
Tomato (summer)	J.I.P.1	—	J.I.P.2	J.I.P.3*

* = 10-inch pots.

In the table above, J.I.P.1 indicates the standard potting compost as given on p. 59, i.e. containing one dose of John Innes base and chalk. J.I.P.2 indicates two doses of the standard amount of base and chalk and J.I.P.3, three doses. Growth in J.I.P.2 or 3 is not necessarily improved or accelerated as compared with J.I.P.1, but it is prolonged, hence feeding need not start so early; the compost "holds" well. If J.I.P.1 has already been mixed it can be converted into J.I.P.2 or 3 in a few moments by adding an extra one or two doses of John Innes base and chalk and mixing thoroughly.

CARNATION BEDS.

The J.I. Composts can be modified for use in carnation beds.

The suggested proportions for moderately heavy soils are 8 parts by bulk of loam, and up to $2\frac{1}{2}$ parts of peat and $1\frac{1}{2}$ parts of coarse sand. For light soils, little or no sand will be required. The peat, however, should not be less than 10% of the whole. The J.I. Base is thoroughly mixed with the loam, peat and sand at the rate of 15 lbs. of base and 3 lbs. of ground chalk, limestone or hydrated lime per cubic yard. Planting may begin a day or two after the beds have been made up. The equivalent rates of application for beds 6 inches deep are $2\frac{1}{2}$ lbs. of J.I. Base and $\frac{1}{2}$ lb. chalk per square yard.

The J.I. Base may also be used for tomatoes and chrysanthemums (Fig. 7) in borders or in the open ground, and for herbaceous borders, summer bedding and the vegetable garden. A suitable rate of application is 2-8 oz. per sq. yard, according to requirements.

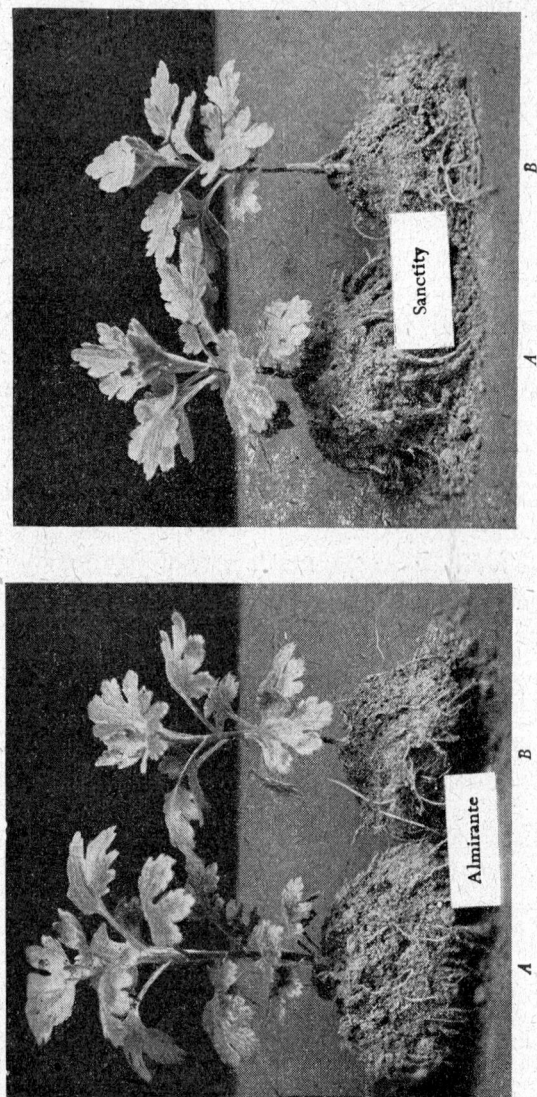

Fig. 7.—*Chrysanthemums bedded in frames.* An experiment comparing two base fertilizers for young chrysanthemums. After three weeks' growth

A. 5½ lbs. of John Innes Base Fertilizer and 1½ lbs. of carbonate of lime per cubic yard of soil
B. 10 lbs. of bone meal and 10 lbs. of carbonate of lime per cubic yard of soil
The recommended amounts are 5 lbs. of John Innes Base Fertilizer and 1 lb. of carbonate of lime per cubic yard of soil

By courtesy of J. B. Stevenson, Esq., Colham Green Nursery, Hillingdon, Middlesex

CHAPTER 9

THE COMPOST : STERILIZATION

THE third of the three requirements for a good compost is, that it should be free from all harmful organisms and substances. Loam and leaf-mould are commonly infested with numerous organisms, some of which are undesirable in pots, others highly injurious, e.g. earthworms, wireworms, eelworms, larvæ of many kinds which prey on the roots of plants and a variety of fungi and micro-organisms. These must be got rid of if we are to have the best possible composts. The process by which this is done is known as *partial sterilization*, often abbreviated to "sterilization."* It should be noted that a soil which is literally sterile and devoid of all life is useless for growing plants ; therefore soil sterilization to be successful must be partial. There are two ways in which partial sterilization can be achieved; by heating the soil, and by the use of chemicals. The former is by far the most efficient method and will be dealt with first.

If soil is heated to temperatures between 120°F. and 212° F. it is altered in three ways, (1) physically, (2) chemically and (3) biologically.

The physical alteration is due to the partial decomposition of the organic matter leaving it in a form more suitable for the bacteria to work upon; and to changes in its colloidal state which result in the soil being easier to wet and more retentive of moisture.

* Pasteurization and disinfestation are other terms in use.

C

The chemical alteration is due to the splitting up of the complex chemical compounds derived from the humus, into simpler compounds which are available as plant food. For example, the total amount of available nitrogenous, phosphatic and potassium compounds is increased, and heated soil is therefore richer than unheated soil as a source of nutrients. This is particularly important in the case of the complex nitrogenous compounds. These, when decomposed by the action of heat, yield ammonia which therefore is found in considerable amount in sterilized soil.

Thirdly, when soil is heated it is altered biologically. As the temperature is raised then, depending on the degree of resistance offered, first one and then another organism is exterminated. Earthworms are killed at about 130° F., the nitrifying bacteria at about 212° F. and all life at 260° F. This differential lethal effect has very important consequences for the gardener. For example, we saw that additional ammonia is formed by chemical processes when soil is heated. But at a temperature of 212° F. the nitrifying bacteria which break down ammonia into nitrate are all killed. Thus in soil heated to boiling point the ammonia remains unchanged and no further production of nitrate takes place. Further, the ammonifying bacteria are not killed at 212° F., so they are able to continue their work of producing ammonia, thus augmenting the supply produced by chemical means. Hence soil heated to this temperature is particularly rich in ammonia and poor in nitrates. Fortunately this absence of nitrates does not matter very much, since most plants apparently take up ammonia freely in the absence of nitrate.

Ammonia in excess, however, has a retarding effect upon seed germination which may sometimes be completely inhibited. Moreover, it seems highly probable that an

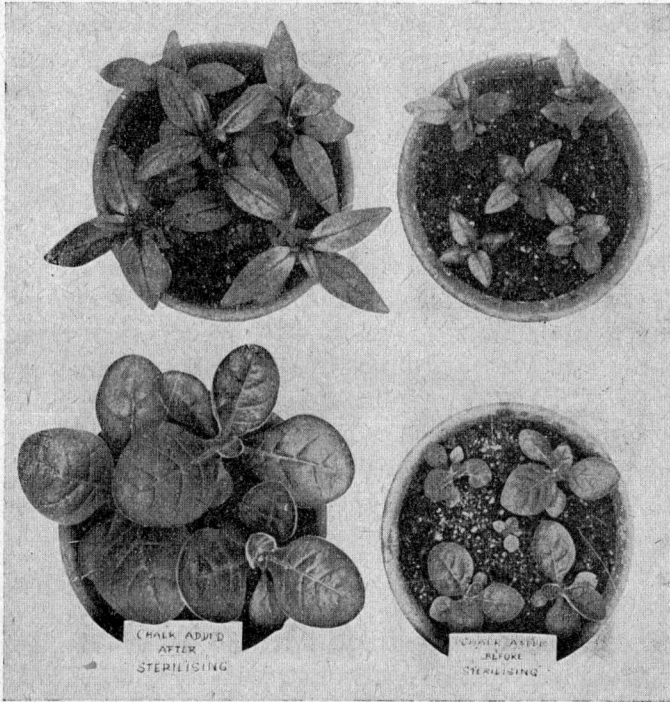

Fig. 8.—*Antirrhinum and tobacco.*

Left : chalk added to the compost after the soil has been **sterilized**
Right : chalk added before sterilization

excess of ammonia also retards seedling growth, although this might also be due to the presence of other toxic substances set free on heating the soil.

The whole of the consequences of heating soil are evidently very complex, nevertheless it is clear that the total amount of available nitrogenous compounds is increased as the temperature is raised and that at a certain point this extra amount may have harmful effects on seed and seedling growth. This increase in available nitrogen depends upon three factors, (1) the nature of the soil, (2) the temperature to which it is heated and (3) the length of time it is heated. Of these, the last is the most important and failure to appreciate it is the main reason why, in the past, sterilized soil has never become popular for the raising of seedlings.

The critical factor involved in the processes giving rise to the sterilizing "check" is the organic content of the soil. If no organic matter is present, a condition never found in horticultural loams, then there is no check, e.g. when clay is heated to red heat no substances harmful to seeds and seedlings are formed. Further, the effect of heat on organic matter is accentuated by the presence of certain minerals, such as lime, which evidently take part in the breakdown of the organic compounds to give substances which in excessive amounts are toxic to young plants (Fig. 8).

Thus, with certain exceptions, the richer a soil is in organic matter, the greater is the amount of available nitrogenous compounds formed when the soil is heated to temperatures exceeding 130° F. Above a certain concentration this extra nitrogen is definitely harmful to germination and seedling growth. Moreover, if organic matter and loam, humus and lime or loam and lime are heated together, or if a compost containing these

materials is sterilized, the amount of available nitrogen
may be still further increased and nitrogen-sensitive
seeds and seedlings harmed in consequence (Fig. 9).
Hence the warning given in the past to leave the

Fig. 9.—*Tobacco, Antirrhinum and Verbena*. Showing the effects of right and wrong
sterilizing. All pans contain the same compost
Top : compost ingredients sterilized separately
Bottom : compost ingredients sterilized together

sterilized soil 3 to 6 weeks "to recover" i.e. to lose
some of its nitrogen, a result which was also achieved
by the heavy watering of seed boxes, etc., in order to
wash out the excess nitrogenous compounds.

Precisely what constitutes a harmful excess of
nitrogen depends upon the species of plant concerned.

Thus tomato and cucumber seedlings may be checked somewhat, but not sufficiently to attract the attention of the grower unless he has a control for purposes of comparison. On the other hand, germination and growth in *Verbena* and *Primula malacoides* are very easily disturbed and the correct sterilization technique must be followed if good results are to be achieved with these plants. Furthermore, what constitutes an overdose of nitrogen for a seedling may be of considerable value to a more mature plant, and far from being noxious, is then highly desirable.

In the course of our experiments it was discovered that the addition of superphosphate to sterilized soil largely counteracted the retarding and injurious effects of soil sterilization (Fig. 10). This is true even when superphosphate is added to the soil before it is sterilized. Hence we may infer that the degree of retardation will depend upon three things, the amounts of (1) organic matter, (2) lime and (3) phosphate present. Retardation will be greatest when the content of organic matter and lime is high and phosphoric acid low. Conversely there will be least retardation when the content of organic matter and lime is low and phosphoric acid high. Thus the sterilization of rich soils is more likely to result in retardation than sterilization of poor soil. As previously pointed out it is possible that other toxic substances besides excess ammonia are concerned in the sterilizing check, but the major factors are certainly those outlined above.

The practical application of these facts is as follows. Turf loam (which is never likely to be too rich in organic matter) should be slightly acid, not alkaline.

Fig. 10.—*Celery*. Showing the importance of adding phosphate to sterilized soil

Middle : normal growth in unsterilized soil
Left : growth checked in sterilized soil
Right : check to growth in sterilized soil immediately eliminated by addition of phosphate

For sterilizing it is better not to use arable soils which
have had heavy dressings of organic material and lime.
Further, if we use peat that is free from all pests and
diseases and therefore does not require sterilization
then we avoid the danger of excess production of
nitrogen which sometimes follows the heating of
organic matter. With these points in mind the obvious
solution to the problem of soil sterilization is to
sterilize the loam separately and not to mix it first with
organic matter or lime.

We have now to consider the second of the three
factors affecting the increase in available nitrogen
following sterilization, namely, to what temperature
should the soil be heated? The figures below provide the
answer. Few bacteria can survive a temperature of
140° F. maintained for 10 minutes. As we saw, however,
the ammonifying bacteria can survive 212° F. They are
able to do this because at one stage of their life cycle
they exist as thick-celled spores and are able to resist the
effects of heating where the thin-walled bacteria
succumb. There is good evidence to show that the
fertility associated with sterilized soils is at least partly
due to the fact that the surviving ammonifying bacteria
propagate themselves with great rapidity, since few or
none of the organisms which prey on them are present
to keep their numbers in check. Most species of fungi
are killed at 170° F. The great majority of viruses are
inactivated at 170° F., but some tobacco viruses (not
found in Britain) are only inactivated at 194° F. Insects
and animal pests and weed seeds are all killed at 170° F.
if this temperature is maintained for 10 minutes.

Thus if the temperature of all the soil is raised to

180°F. for 10 minutes there is small chance of any pest or disease surviving. This should be regarded as the minimum sterilizing temperature. If superphosphate is added to the soil after sterilization then the presence of harmful substances is reduced to a minimum and the soil is both clean and safe (Fig. 11).

The remaining point to be settled is the length of

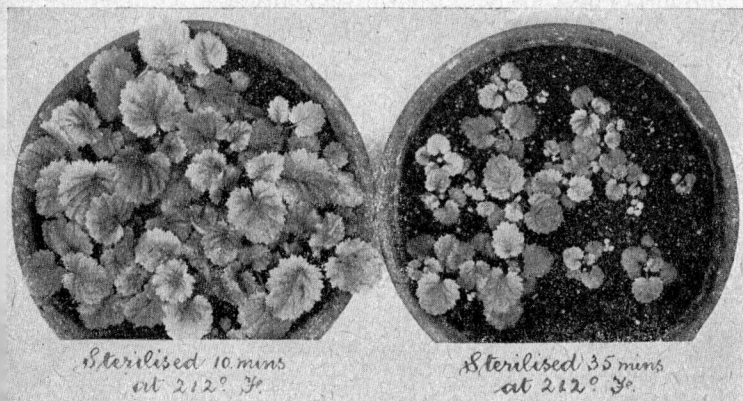

Sterilised 10 mins at 212° F.　　Sterilised 35 mins at 212° F.

Fig. 11.—*Primula malacoides*. Showing ill effects of prolonged heating of soil

time the soil should be heated to secure the maximum amount of nitrogen compatible with good germination and growth. We cannot too strongly emphasize that prolonged heating of the soil is by far the commonest cause of unsatisfactory germination and seedling growth in sterilized soils. There are many good gardeners who tried sterilized soil in the past and gave it up because they were following methods suitable for gross feeding plants like tomato and chrysanthemum, but wholly unsuitable for many of the less vigorous plants normally raised from seed. As previously shown (p. 70) the increase in available nitrogen following prolonged heating of the soil may be advantageous to strong growing plants, but in the majority of cases germination and seedling growth are retarded and may even be inhibited. Hence the tomato grower might with impunity heat his beds for 40 to 60 minutes, a procedure the raiser of *Primula malacoides* dare not follow (Fig. 11). "One man's meat is another man's poison" applies also to plants.

Ignoring for the moment the time required to heat the soil to sterilizing temperature, our experiments have shown that 10 minutes at 180° F. is enough for both seed and potting composts. Ideally *the temperature of the soil should be raised as quickly as possible* to the desired maximum and after sterilizing is finished the hot soil should be immediately removed and spread out thinly for rapid cooling.

If the time taken to reach sterilizing temperature is relatively long as in low-pressure steaming, then the soil should not be heated for the further 10 minutes, but removed and cooled at once.

OBJECT OF SOIL STERILIZATION

Summarizing the foregoing remarks, the object of soil sterilisation is twofold :

1. To eliminate all harmful organisms.

2. To secure the maximum amount of nitrogen compatible with good germination and growth.

TECHNIQUE OF SOIL STERILIZATION

The correct technique therefore of soil sterilization is:

1. Heat the soil as rapidly as possible to the sterilizing temperature.

2. Maintain this temperature no longer than is necessary.

3. In so far as it is necessary, sterilize the compost ingredients separately (see p. 76).

4. Add fertilizers to the sterilized soil, to rectify the unbalance following sterilization and to make good the natural deficiency of plant foods.

As a general rule, the minimum sterilizing temperature is 180°F. maintained for 10 minutes, but these figures have to be modified a little according to the method of sterilization employed (p. 93).

STERILIZATION OF COMPOST MATERIALS

As previously explained, a harmful excess of nitrogen may be made available when certain materials are sterilized separately, or when certain combinations of materials, are sterilized together. These are listed below :

These may be sterilized together.	No two of these may be sterilized together.	These need not be sterilized.
Loam Sand	Loam Leaf-mould Manure Fertilizers Lime	Clean Sand Moss-peat Sedge-peat Fertilizers Lime

Second-Soil*

We have seen that germination and seedling growth may be retarded in composts which have been sterilized as such. Now, "second-soil" is a compost, therefore if it is sterilized, a harmful reaction may result. The degree of this reaction will vary according to the organic matter-lime-phosphoric-acid ratio of the compost. Since second soils vary greatly in this respect, it is impossible to predict the results of sterilizing a particular sample. As a general rule, therefore, *it is safer not to sow seeds in sterilized second soil*. It can be used, however, for pricking out and potting on. In most cases, if not all, fertilizers should be added as for the potting compost.

Chemical Sterilization

The effects of chemical sterilization compare closely with those obtained when soil is heated to 140° F., at which low temperature a number of pests and diseases survive treatment. There is little chemical decom-

---

* Soil which has previously been used for growing pot plants

position of the organic matter and the amount of ammonia is increased owing to the extermination of organisms detrimental to the ammonifying bacteria. There is no sterilizing check as with heated soil, but great care must be taken to ensure that fumes do not remain in the soil after treatment, otherwise both germination and seedling growth may be retarded. Fertilizers should be added to chemically sterilized soils in the usual way to make up for the natural deficiency of plant foods.

CHAPTER 10

STERILIZING APPARATUS

Low-Pressure Steaming

WE have already seen that *the ideal method of soil sterilization is to raise the temperature as quickly as possible to sterilizing point and to maintain this temperature for as short a period as is compatible with the killing of all harmful organisms without producing an excess of active nitrogen compounds.*

Now in low-pressure steaming it is impossible to raise the temperature of a reasonable bulk of soil to 180–200° F. in much less than 30 to 40 minutes and in order to equal these figures the design of the apparatus must be very good. The general principles fundamental to low-pressure steam sterilization are—

1. As large an area of soil as possible should be exposed to the steam, and

2. The total bulk of soil should be kept small enough to permit reaching a temperature of 180° F. in about 45 minutes.

The simplest type of low-pressure steam sterilizer has only three essential parts; a fire box or other heating element, a container for water resting upon it, and a soil container with a perforated bottom fitting tightly into the water container to ensure that all the steam passes through the soil. The efficiency of the apparatus depends on three things. Firstly the perforations in the soil container should be as numerous as possible, covering the whole of the bottom. Secondly the container must be of relatively large area and shallow. Thirdly the source of heat should be powerful to ensure the rapid generation of steam. As an example of the second point, a container $22'' \times 20'' \times 5''$ holds a bushel of soil, so does a container $22'' \times 10'' \times 10''*$ but the former will heat up more quickly than the latter and the soil will in consequence keep much drier. The longer steam is applied the wetter the soil will be when taken from the sterilizer, owing to condensation.

Fig. 12.—A simple method of adapting a domestic copper for the sterilization of small quantities of soil

i. *Saucepan.*

The simplest way of sterilizing small quantities of soil

* It is not suggested that these are suitable dimensions.

is to use a large saucepan. About half an inch of water is put in the saucepan which is then filled loosely with *dust-dry* soil. The soil should have been previously sifted through a $\frac{1}{4}$ inch sieve to get rid of stones and lumps. The gas is then turned up high for a few minutes until the water boils, and then it is allowed to simmer for fifteen minutes. The soil will be sterilized in about twenty minutes from the start. It is then turned out on to a clean surface to let the excess moisture evaporate. Using a six-pint saucepan, three lots of soil can be sterilized in one hour, which is enough to make four gallons of potting compost.

ii. *Domestic Copper.*

Larger quantities of soil can be sterilized in the following way. One to two gallons of water are poured into a domestic copper. About two inches over this water, a bucket perforated all over with $\frac{1}{8}$ inch holes about two inches apart, is supported on an open framework which allows the steam to reach all parts of the bucket (Fig. 12). Two gallons of *dry*, sifted loam are placed in the bucket and the gas is then turned on full: if a fire is used for heating it should be bright and "drawing" strongly. On test it was found that the water boiled in 10 minutes and the soil was at a temperature of 200°F. 30 minutes later. A further five minutes steaming should be ample for sterilizing this quantity of soil. Coarse sacking may be used in place of a bucket with excellent results.

iii. *Proprietary Sterilizers.*

Small proprietary low-pressure sterilizers are advertised to sterilize soil in about one hour. They are made in a variety of sizes with soil capacities from 1 to 3 bushels.* Larger models hold from 4 to 18 bushels. The efficiency of the latter is somewhat variable, e.g. one is advertised to sterilize 10 bushels of soil in 50 to 60 minutes, another 8 bushels in 180 minutes.

Since in low-pressure sterilizers at least 45 to 60 minutes are required to raise the temperature of the soil to 180°F., once this temperature has been reached the sterilizer should be emptied immediately. There is no advantage whatever in exceeding this figure or in prolonging the period of heating. *A thermometer should always be used for measuring the temperature of the soil*, especially the top inch or two and in the corners. In the case of sterilizers with a metal lid, the soil will be kept drier if covered with heavy sacking, which will absorb condensed moisture dropping from the lid.

iv. *The John Innes Sterilizer*

The J.I. Sterilizer (Fig. 13) has been designed for the grower who wants to build a sterilizer of high efficiency, moderate size and low cost. Proprietary low pressure sterilizers are usually made of metal, consequently they lose much of their heat to the air instead of to the soil. Moreover metal is costly and liable to corrode too quickly for the grower's pocket.

* Since gardeners always make up their composts by bulk, it is highly desirable that the size of soil sterilizers should be given in terms of capacity, i.e. gallons, bushels (8 gallons) or yards (21 bushels), and not as in some proprietary sterilizers, by the weight of soil they contain.

The John Innes Sterilizer therefore was designed with four objects in mind:

1. *Heating efficiency;*
2. *Strength of construction;*
3. *Durability of materials;*
4. *Low cost.*

Fig. 13.—The John Innes Sterilizer

Maximum heating efficiency is obtained by exposing the largest possible area of soil to the steam which heats it; and by the employment of good insulating materials to prevent the loss of heat to the outside air. These requirements are met by the use of bricks for the main constructional work. This is of a simple character and can be done by any handy man on the nursery, hence costs are low. The sterilizer holds half a cubic yard of soil (10½ bushels) which, under average conditions, is sterilized in 30 to 40 minutes.*

Satisfactory results can be obtained with low-pressure steam sterilizers if they are used in an intelligent way. The chief points to observe are these: *use soil which is dry* and which has been stored in a warm place; cold, wet soil will take much longer to sterilize than soil which is warm and comparatively dry. *Don't overload the sterilizer* and don't use the portable models in a draughty place.

High-Pressure Steaming

High-pressure steaming is unquestionably the most efficient method of soil sterilization. It has all the advantages of other methods without any of their disadvantages. Unfortunately, the cost of apparatus is relatively high, but this is more than offset by the large amount of soil that can be sterilized in a given time. For instance, an 80 lb. pressure plant serving two half-yard sterilizing bins will sterilize at least one yard (21 bushels) of soil per hour. By comparison a large portable low-pressure plant is advertised to sterilize 18 bushels in three hours. High-pressure steaming is therefore especially suitable for the grower who at

---

* The cost in 1947 was £39. The specification and building instructions are given in "The Fruit and the Soil: the John Innes Collected Leaflets" published by Oliver & Boyd, Edinburgh.

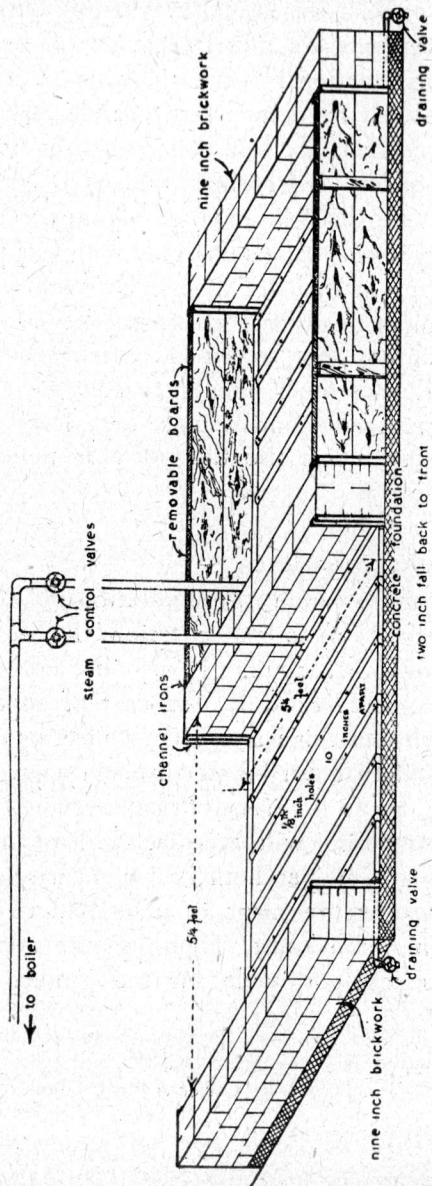

Fig. 14.—High-Pressure Steam Sterilizing lay-out of two sterilizing bins, each holding one cubic yard of soil

certain seasons must sterilize large quantities of soil
as quickly as he can.

A reconditioned boiler, capable of generating steam
at 80 lbs. pressure in sufficient quantity to sterilize
2 yards of soil per hour, complete with steam pipes,
valves, grids and injector costs £80-90* or about $300
in U.S.A. A smaller model† working at the same
pressure but dealing with one yard of soil per hour costs
£60-70.* Both these prices include erection costs.

High-pressure apparatus consists of a boiler from
which steam is led to a grid of perforated pipes placed
in the bottom of the sterilizing bins (Fig. 14). Since
the depth of soil to be sterilized *should not exceed 12
inches*, a bin of one yard capacity must be five feet three
inches square. The efficiency of working depends a great
deal on the design of the sterilizing bins. The side
walls should be constructed of nine-inch brick work,
on a concrete foundation. The fronts and backs of the
bins are closed with detachable boards which drop
into channel irons fixed to the walls. To allow condensed
moisture to drain away, the floors of the bins have a
fall of two inches from back to front. The water which
collects in the pipes from condensation of the steam
must be got rid of by means of draining valves (see
Fig. 14), otherwise the passage of the steam will be
blocked. The sloping of the bin floors and pipes is an
important factor in keeping the soil in a dry condition.
The correct spacing of the grid pipes and the holes in
them is essential for securing an even distribution of
steam. In a bin five feet three inches square, 7 grid
pipes will be needed $\frac{3}{4}$ inch inside diameter, and placed

* Pre-war figures.   † A suitable boiler size is 7 ft. × 3 ft.

10 inches between the centres. The pipes are connected to the $1\frac{1}{4}$ inch main pipe at the side of the bin (Fig. 14). The grid pipes are drilled with $\frac{1}{8}$ inch holes at 10 inch spacing along the top. It may be advisable to drill extra holes in the pipes at the corners of the bins which in practice are usually the last to heat up.

To carry out high-pressure sterilizing efficiently a definite method of working should be followed. First *the loam should be dry*; in order to get it into this condition it may be necessary to protect it with a tarpaulin or other cover some weeks before it is wanted.

All the soil should be riddled before it is steamed in order to break it down into small pieces. Large lumps may not sterilize properly. A friable soil can be sifted through a $\frac{3}{8}$ inch sieve, but heavier loams of a fibrous nature are more troublesome, and may have to be put through a $1\frac{1}{2}$ inch sieve before sterilizing and through the $\frac{3}{8}$ inch sieve afterwards. With heavy loams the sifting must not be left too long after sterilizing, otherwise the lumps of soil dry out and become too hard to sift easily. Fill the sterilizing bins loosely with the sifted soil to a depth of twelve inches and level it off without compacting it. Cover the soil with heavy sacking and turn the steam full on until the temperature of *all* the soil is at least 180°F. This takes about five minutes for half a yard of soil and up to 10 minutes for a yard, working at a pressure of 80 lbs. The steam is then shut off and the soil allowed to stand a further 10 minutes. Even after standing 10 minutes the temperature falls little below 180°F. The advantage of this method of sterilizing by residual heat is that the soil comes out of the bins very much drier than when steam is blown through it continuously for the whole period. In addition steam and fuel are economized and if several sterilizing bins are available a large amount of soil can be handled very speedily. It is most important that the temperature of the soil should be measured accurately with a thermometer and not guessed. A suitable stem or chemical thermometer costs only 3/6 or $1 in U.S.A.

Other points to watch in the working of high-pressure apparatus are as follows. Stoke up the fire a little at a time between steamings so that a good hot fire is available when it is wanted. Use the steam injector immediately after steaming so that the cold water is brought to the boil before the next steaming commences. When emptying the hot soil always shovel along the bottom. *Never push the shovel into the hot, moist soil from above,* as this compacts it and produces lumps which harden on drying.

The high-pressure boiler may also be used for sterilizing pots. A pipe is run from the boiler to the bottom of a large galvanized water tank. The pipe terminates in a horizontal, perforated arm through which steam is blown. A piece of duck-board covers the bottom of the tank and the arm, and on this the pots are tightly packed layer upon layer. The pots are then covered with *cold* water and the steam turned on until the temperature rises to 200°F. The steam is then turned off and the water drained away by means of a cock fixed at the bottom of the tank. Pots should not be put into boiling water or many may be cracked.

ELECTRIC STERILIZERS

Electric sterilizers are of two kinds. One employs the heating-element principle in which the current passes through resistance heating-wires enclosed in tubes running through the soil at distances varying between 6 and 8 inches. The disadvantage of this type of electric sterilizer is that uneven heating occurs. The soil in contact with the tubes becomes hot before the main body of soil, which heats only by conduction. Its advantages are that it has a definite and known current demand, and all soils, regardless of their nature, can be treated similarly. This type of electric sterilizer is used extensively in America, but so far as we are aware is not manufactured in Britain.

In the second type of sterilizer the soil is placed between metal plates or electrodes and is heated by the resistance it offers to the current flowing from one plate to the other. This type of electrode sterilizer has many advantages over that employing the heating element principle. The soil heats up uniformly, a most important feature, and overheating cannot occur. The layer of soil in contact with the electrode plates loses its moisture when the temperature reaches 180°F. to 200°F., and in consequence, the electrical resistance is sufficiently increased to prevent a further rise in temperature unless more water is added. We have seen that a temperature of 180°F., maintained for 10 minutes, is sufficient to destroy all the organisms harmful to plant growth, therefore the fact that boiling point cannot be reached in an electrode type sterilizer does not impair its efficiency. Its chief disadvantage is that the current demand varies considerably with the type of soil to be sterilized. It also varies as the soil heats up, the final demand being three to four times the initial demand. With rich soils it may on occasion rise above the load allowed by the electric service.

In practice, differences between soils can be met by adding water to those of high electrical resistance, and/or by reducing the distance between the electrode plates. As a grower is likely to use only one or two types of soil, these adjustments are soon determined. Contrary to practice with steam sterilizers the soil should be firmly compacted in electrical types to decrease electrical resistance. Sand, of course, has a high resistance and if the grower wishes to sterilize it he must first mix it with the loam and then sterilize these materials together.

Electrode Type Sterilizers

These sterilizers are on sale, varying in soil capacity from $2\frac{1}{2}$ gallons to 24 bushels, and can be arranged to operate on A.C. or D.C. supply. The time required to sterilize is about one hour in the case of the smallest size and from 1 hour to 2 hours for the larger models.

The $2\frac{1}{2}$ and 8 gallon sizes are especially useful to the amateur gardener as they can be plugged in to the domestic heating supply. The average maximum demand is 10 amps. The soil container in some models is made without a fixed bottom and rests on a special shovelling board from which it is lifted when sterilization is completed.

Electrical contacts on the removable lid ensure safety, as the supply of current is cut off when the lid is removed. The eight and the twenty gallon sizes are made with a central electrode plate to be used for soils of high resistance. Several models of built-in sterilizers are available holding from eight gallons to twenty-four bushels of soil. The types suitable for the small grower are constructed to form a continuation of the existing potting shed bench. Intermediate electrode plates are used and only one side of the soil container need be filled when small quantities of soil are required. It should be noted that electric sterilizers of over eight gallons capacity cannot be used on the ordinary domestic heating circuit.

The larger built-in types are made in three sizes, 8, 16 and 24 bushel capacity and are especially suitable for large growers. They have a maximum demand, varying between 30 and 60 amps., and cannot be used except on 400 volt single- or three-phase circuits. These large sterilizers have an arrangement of three compartments each holding $\frac{1}{3}$ of the charge of soil, the sides comprising the electrode plates from which the current passes during sterilization. Intermediate plates can be fitted to speed up the process of heating when required, and these may be cut off by hand or automatically at any predetermined temperature. Other kinds of electric sterilizers are the skip and wheelbarrow types, made in capacities varying from about 4 to 24 bushels, and having maximum demands of 30 to 60 amps. It will be seen that where electric current is available at low rates it offers a clean, cheap and efficient form of sterilization. Electric sterilizers cannot be used for sterilizing pots for which separate provision must be made.

Baking

One of the earliest methods of soil sterilization was by baking. Experimenters soon discovered that baked soil had harmful effects on seed germination and early seedling growth. This result is often due to the soil being heated to temperatures in excess of 212°F. in those parts of the soil closest to the fire or flue. At such high temperatures the humus of the soil is partly destroyed and its physical condition impaired. Even if the maximum temperature is kept below 212°F., the heating is very uneven and difficult to control and for these reasons we do not recommend this method of sterilization where plants are to be raised from seed.

Baking is used by some growers with apparent success. However, it will be found in such cases that either the plants being raised are strong growers like tomato, or the baking temperatures are kept so low as to run the risk of under sterilization.

A modification of the older dry-baking system is the semi-steaming method of heating which consists in adding an inch or two of water, according to the size of the apparatus, to the bottom of the soil container. On heating, a good deal of steam is generated and passes upwards to the top layers of soil. This method minimizes to a great extent the danger of overheating common to ordinary baking.

Ignoring the capital outlay the advantages and disadvantages of the various methods of soil sterilization may be briefly summarized as follows. High-pressure steam sterilizing is the most efficient method and may be taken as the standard. By comparison, low-pressure steam, baking, and electric sterilizers are slower in heating up and cannot be loaded or unloaded so quickly. The large capacity electric sterilizers are quicker in operation than the average low pressure steam models. The electric models, which are excellently constructed also have the advantage of being very clean and convenient to operate, and thus recommend themselves especially to amateurs.

Unsatisfactory results in the use of soil sterilizers may be attributed to one or more of the following causes.

LOW-PRESSURE STEAM STERILIZERS

1. Soil too wet when loaded into the sterilizer.
2. Soil too firm.
3. Sterilizer overloaded.
4. Sterilizer badly designed.

HIGH PRESSURE STEAM STERILIZERS

1. Soil too wet when loaded into sterilizer.
2. Sterilizer overloaded.
3. Too low a steam pressure.
4. Too small a boiler to maintain a proper pressure.
5. Water or soil blocking grid pipes.
6. Not enough holes in grid pipes.

ELECTRIC STERILIZERS

1. Soil does not heat up.

    See fuses have not blown. If fuses intact try

adding more water to the soil and see that it is firmly compacted; or if electrodes are adjustable, place them closer together. If soil still does not heat up, and there is no shorting, it may be concluded that its resistance is too high for proper working (e.g. sand or undecomposed leaves).

Note:—Soils of high resistance will sometimes heat up if watered with a solution of 1 oz. of superphosphate to a gallon of water.

2. Fuse persistently blows.

Soil is too wet or has very low resistance (e.g. stable manure). Try adjusting the electrodes to widest spacing and avoid compacting the soil more than is necessary.

SUMMARY OF TYPES AND METHODS

Type of sterilizer.	Capacity.	Average time of sterilizing.	End temperature.	Soil put in sterilizer.
Saucepan	4-8 pints	20 min.	About 200° F.	Sifted, dust-dry and loose.
Domestic Copper	¼ bushel	30-40 min.	About 200° F.	Sifted, dry and loose
Proprietary Models	1 bushel to ¾ yard	1-2 hr.	180° F.	Sifted, dry and loose
John Innes Sterilizer	½ yard	30-40 min.	180° F.	Sifted, dry and loose
High Press. Sterilizer	1-2 yards	15-20 min.	180-212° F.	Sifted, dry and loose
Electric Models	¼ bushel to 1 yard	60-90 min.	180° F.	Sifted, firmed then watered

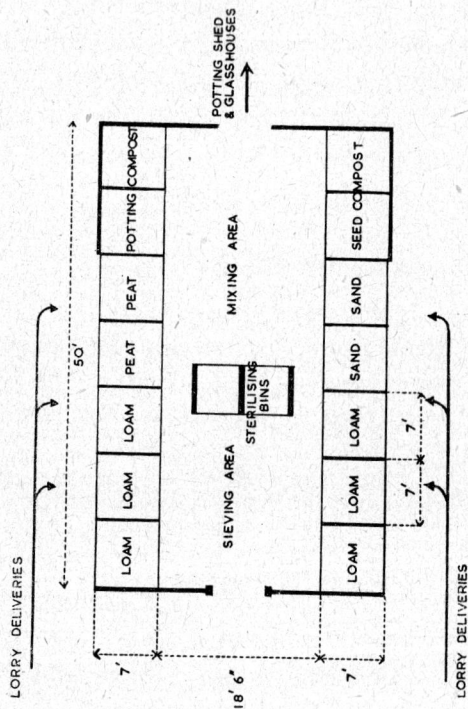

Fig. 15.

The Sterilizing Shed

Large amounts of soil cannot be sterilized with economy unless a spacious shed is available for this one special purpose. The lay out of this shed is worth serious consideration, since practically all of the labour involved is in moving soil from one place to another. To minimise this, the unsterilized loam is stacked near the sterilizing bins, and the peat and sand, which do not require sterilizing, near the mixing floor. Thus, as these materials are successively handled they are moved towards the other end of the shed where they are composted, and/or stored (Fig. 15). In particular the shed should be conceived as being in two parts, the unsterilized and sterilized sections separated by the sterilizing plant. Designs will vary according to local conditions but the principle will be clear from the diagram on the previous page.

CHAPTER II

CHEMICAL METHODS OF STERILIZATION

WHERE steam apparatus or electricity is not available for sterilizing purposes a number of chemical substances may be used as substitutes. Chemical control of certain soil pests was practised many years ago in France, when carbon-di-sulphide was injected into the soil to control *Phylloxera* of the grape vine. It was extensively used for a time but soon lost favour with the growers. The chemical was cheap but its vapour did not penetrate well in some soils and where penetration was good it was too readily lost by evaporation and diffusion to be really effective. This illustrates fairly accurately the requirements of a chemical sterilizer. To be effective it must penetrate the soil rapidly to a sufficient depth, must remain toxic long enough to kill all organisms harmful to plant growth, must not leave behind any substances deleterious to plants, and must maintain the physical condition of the soil.

No gases heavy enough to sink into soil have yet been found to meet these requirements, but a number of chemicals and proprietary substances in liquid form are of value in the absence of better methods of soil sterilization. All, however, possess one serious disadvantage in that their efficiency depends on thoroughly wetting every particle of soil. This may not be a serious consideration when treating borders, but it is a drawback with seed and potting soils. The physical condition of the soil is impaired, apart from the necessity of re-drying, which involves considerable loss of time. It is doubtful if any chemical applied as a drench fulfils all the conditions of efficient sterilization so well as heating methods.

A large number of chemicals have been used in recent years for sterilizing soils; we need only consider three, formaldehyde, cresylic acid and coal- or tar-oil derivatives. It is incorrect to speak of naphthalene, which is a soil fumigant, or corrosive sublimate, which is a fungicide, as being capable of partial sterilization although they are often advertised as such.

Commercial formaldehyde (formalin) is sold as a 38 per cent. to 40 per cent. pure solution. For sterilizing purposes this should be diluted to a 2 per cent. solution by adding one part to 49 parts of water, and applied at the rate of one gallon per bushel of soil. After treatment the soil should be covered to keep in the volatile gas for a further 48 hours, then spread out as thinly as possible to dry. Formaldehyde is highly toxic to plant life and the treated soil cannot be used until all traces of the gas have disappeared. The soil should be treated in an open shed, as the gas is dangerous to workers at too high concentrations. Formaldehyde is the most extensively used chemical soil sterilizing agent; as a fungicide it is efficient, but unfortunately it has little if any value as an insecticide. Further its use may cause retardation and reduction in the germination of delicate seeds.

Cresylic acid (liquid carbolic acid) sold as a 97 per

D

cent. to 99 per cent. pure solution is a product of the crude tar acids. Its use as a soil sterilizer has been recommended for some 30 years. The acid must be diluted to a $2\frac{1}{2}$ per cent. solution by adding 1 gallon to 39 gallons of water. This is applied at the rate of 1 gallon of solution to 1 bushel of soil. The treated soil is then covered for a further 48 hours and spread out thinly to dry. After a period of three weeks it is ready for use. Workers handling cresylic acid must wear rubber gloves and avoid spilling any of the acid on their clothes. Cresylic acid can be recommended as a sterilizing agent where the growers aim is to destroy soil pests, but it has little value as a fungicide.

The coal- and tar-oil derivatives are sold under proprietary names. Although extravagant claims are sometimes made for them, they fulfil all that can be expected from liquid sterilization. In all cases the directions given by the makers must be explicitly followed.

Before using liquid sterilizers the soil is best sieved to remove lumps large enough to escape thorough soaking. It should be in a moist condition as neither very dry nor very wet soils can be efficiently treated. The treatment must be thorough in all cases and every particle of soil drenched.

In comparison with the use of steam or electricity, liquid sterilization is cheaper, as, of course, no apparatus of any kind is required.

CHAPTER 12

THE FEEDING OF POT PLANTS

IN earlier chapters we have discussed the food supply of the plant in relation to composts. It will be readily understood that sufficient food to last all the plant's life cannot be added to the potting compost. The small amount of food required by the seedling is amply provided by the seed compost, but as its food requirements increase it is necessary to transfer the seedling to the richer potting compost in order to maintain uninterrupted growth. The vigorous plant soon uses up the nitrogen, phosphate and potash contained in the small amount of soil in a pot, and these elements must be regularly replaced if a normal growth rate is to be maintained. The only way this can be done is by adding fertilizers, either dry or dissolved in water. It is the current practice, however, to use different fertilizers for different plants, and the gardener is offered a large array of fertilizers specially compounded for chrysanthemums, carnations, roses, tomatoes, etc. Since it has been found possible to devise a standard base-fertilizer for inclusion in the potting compost which would satisfy the requirements of the great majority of plants, it followed that a standard fertilizer could be devised for the after feeding of pot plants.

In the potting compost the proportions of the nutrients supplied by the fertilizers were approximately 1 of nitrogen, $1\frac{1}{4}$ of phosphoric acid and 2 of potash.

Pot-bound plants, however, require considerably more nitrogen and to meet this the proportion of nitrogen must be increased.

Tests have shown that only one feed is necessary and the great variety of fertilizers (including manure water) for feeding pot plants is redundant. The John Innes Feed is a quick-acting fertilizer with a balance of approximately 3 nitrogen, 1 phosphoric acid and 1 potash. It is suitable for all kinds of *pot-bound* plants, but in the case of tomatoes a potash feed should be given occasionally.

The J.I. Feed is sold in two forms, "L" for liquid "D" for dry feeding. The formulae and other details are given below.

	"L" for liquid feeding	"D" for dry feeding
Formula, parts by weight.	15.00 Ammonium sulphate 2.75 Potass. nitrate 2.25 Mono-ammonium phosphate	The same as "L" but mixed with a carrier *
Rate of application	½ to 1 oz. per gallon of (preferably soft) water. Use fresh.	½ to 1 teaspoonful per 5-in. pot
Analyses: Nitrogen Soluble phosphoric acid. Pure potash	18.65 6.20 6.20	6.80 1.94 1.94

* Owing to difficulties of mixing it is not recommended that gardeners attempt to make up the "D" feed for themselves.

Control $\frac{1}{4}$ oz. per gallon   1 oz. per gallon

Fig. 16.—*Petunia*. The rate of application of the John Innes Feed must be increased to 1 oz. per gallon (rightmost box) for the feeding of crowded boxes. The plants on the left have not been fed.

The "L" feed is composed entirely of plant foods and dissolved in soft water leaves no sediment. For general purposes it is used at the rate of $\frac{1}{2}$ oz. to 1 gallon of water, about once a week; for frequent application $\frac{1}{4}$ oz. to 1 gallon of water. For vigorous plants and crowded boxes, 1 oz. per gallon of water every ten days or according to requirements (Fig. 15). It should be used within 24 hours of mixing, or some of the phosphate will be precipitated and will no longer be available. The "D" feed is used at the rate of $\frac{1}{2}$ teaspoonful to a 48 pot once every 14 or 21 days, according to requirements. It should be watered in well.

The feeds have been used for a wide variety of plants and have given excellent results in conjunction with the John Innes composts for which they are specifically designed. It must not be assumed that they will be equally effective with other composts.

PRINCIPLES OF FEEDING

The first few feeds should be given at intervals of 14-21 days according to weather and other conditions, gradually shortening the period as the plants develop. We have fed strong growing plants with the liquid feed at every watering for three months, excepting at week-ends, when they were watered with plain water. Plants vary in their requirements and discretion must be used as to the frequency of feeding and the number of feeds given. For instance, the strong growing chrysanthemum will require more frequent feeding than the comparatively weak-growing primula.

The period that elapses between the final potting and the commencement of feeding will not be the same for all plants. It will depend not only on the kind of plant but upon the season during which it is grown. The symptoms of food deficiency outlined in Chapter 2 do not develop appreciably until the plant is past the stage where it can be "pulled round" to normal again by feeding. Therefore, the man who wishes to grow good pot plants must be guided more by the amount of roots formed and less by the foliage. When the roots have penetrated well into the new soil then the grower must watch the foliage most carefully, especially the lower leaves for the faintest signs of starvation. Indeed, *the whole art of correct feeding lies in being able to anticipate the exact moment it should begin*, so that no symptoms whatever of starvation appear. The average gardener does not appreciate fully the fact that there must be no check to growth from the earliest days to maturity, if the plant is to be well grown and healthy. To wait until pots are filled with roots generally means that the plant suffers a more or less severe check which can be avoided by earlier feeding. For example, we find that plants of *Primula sinensis* having their final shift in late August require feeding some five weeks later. This period is a short one, but root growth in the John Innes composts is always rapid.

The use of stable or farmyard manure-water has been abandoned, in the first place because it is not sterile and would possibly introduce disease organisms into the sterilized composts; secondly because its value varies with the quality of the manure from which it is made, and thirdly because the balance of nutrients it contains is not the best. By comparison we have in the standard feed a fertilizer of known analysis, unvarying quality and the right balance. And so the smelly manure water tank, the breeding ground of pests and diseases, must give way to the clean and pleasant chemical solution.

CHAPTER 13

GLASSHOUSE HYGIENE

IF the full benefit is to be had from the use of the improved composts described in this book, consideration must be given to the more general matters of plant cultivation under glass, and especially to hygiene. The object of hygiene is prevention rather than cure. It is foolish, for example, to put sterilized soil into unsterilized pots, or to use unsterilized leaves for covering the crocks.

We are convinced that many of the troubles which come to gardeners, private, municipal and commercial, are the result of neglect or misunderstanding, either in regard to cultural methods or the training of the staff.

> " All along o' dirtiness, all along o' mess,
>   All along o' doing things rather-more-or-less."

Dirty water tanks and potting benches which are dumping grounds for every sort of rubbish, diseased plants which are allowed to stand in the houses or frames to contaminate the rest of the crop, over-crowding of plants—these are the sort of things that commonly cause trouble. Further, no one can expect a member of the staff to be particular about one thing (sterilized soil) if he is told, or allowed to think, that it does not matter at all what he does about other things (dirty tanks etc.) We must be consistent if we are to expect consistent results. Attention to detail often makes all the difference between failure and success.

In this chapter we propose to deal briefly with those details which demand special attention. In the aggregate they appear to make heavy demands on time, labour and money, but we have proved conclusively that this is not the case. The suggestions which follow are of the simplest character and do not necessitate the purchase of expensive materials. Incorporated as part of the normal routine they take very little extra time or labour, and once the staff have been clearly instructed in these methods and have got used to them, the wheels run very smoothly indeed. Hygiene under glass is a question of clean habits, and habits are the outcome of a way of thinking. "It doesn't matter", "so-and-so doesn't do it", " the old ways are good enough for me" all betoken the bad gardener and ultimately, the man who will complain at his misfortune after having done everything to deserve it.

POTTING SHEDS

The average potting shed is a depressing place, badly lighted, badly designed and extremely untidy. There is no excuse for this state of affairs since an excellent building can be erected at moderate cost. The essential lay-out is simple. A longish run of well lighted bench down one side of the shed, preferably on the north or east sides. Rough one inch flooring supported on a 3 in. × 2 in. framework and covered with $\frac{1}{4}$ inch rubber flooring makes a first rate bench, which can be washed down with ease, is resilient and not so liable to break pots when knocking out plants for repotting. Such a bench is no dearer than the ordinary potting bench and its life is indefinitely long. On the other side of the shed are the pot racks for clean sterilized pots, each size in its appropriate rack. These should always be kept well supplied with pots. A roomy cupboard is essential to hold small tools, fertilizers, seed pockets, labels etc., and other sundries which are in constant use. The space below the benches can be used for storing seed boxes, large pots, etc. Stocks of sterilized sand for propagating purposes, sterilized moss for the bottoms of pots, sterilized crocks, etc., can be accommodated in small dust-bins below the benches. Sieves and shovels should each have their appropriate place on the walls.

The potting shed should contain only those things which are absolutely essential to the business of potting and these in as clean a condition as possible. Dirty pots, etc., should not be allowed to accumulate, but removed outside after repotting plants, and *unsterilized soil, soil from outdoors and second soil should never be kept or used on the same bench as sterilized soil*. At the end of each day the shed should be tidied up and everything left in good order. If these points are observed, orderly and clean habits soon take the place of disorderliness and dirtiness, and a higher standard of hygiene is thereby established.

Glasshouses

Have the largest possible panes of glass and see that the side glazing runs right down to bench level. Light in winter is too precious to lose through bad glasshouse construction. Paint the interior white to get the maximum reflection of light. With the possible exception of conservatories, no plants should be allowed to grow under the benches, or pests and diseases will be encouraged. The best finish for the ground beneath the benches is 2 to 3 inches of dust free $\frac{1}{2}$ inch clinker. This not only retains moisture very well, but is uncongenial to worms and woodlice and does not encourage the growth of weeds. For similar reasons the best material for covering the benches is $\frac{3}{8}$ inch dust free clinker. Chippings may look better but they are inferior in all other respects.

Have the water tanks in such a position that no drainage water can run into them from the paths or benches. It is the height of folly to allow water that has run through pots to find its way back into the tank. Water tanks must be kept scrupulously clean and not used as dumps for broken pots or soil; the practice of dipping plants in the tank, too, is a bad one. Green algæ often grow on the sides of tanks and become a nuisance by blocking up the roses of water cans. Periodic emptying of the tanks and watering the sides with a solution of copper sulphate, at $\frac{1}{4}$ lb. to 1 gallon of water will kill the algæ and sterilize the tank at the same time. The greatest care must be taken to see that every trace of this solution, which is highly dangerous to plants, is removed by mopping out and thoroughly rinsing with clean water before refilling the tanks. If rain water is collected from the glasshouse roofs for watering, then the gutters must be kept clear of mud, decayed leaves etc.

At least once every year the glasshouse should be

cleared of plants and thoroughly cleaned down. If disease has been present the house should be sterilized by thoroughly wetting the sides, benches, pipes and floors with a 2 per cent. solution of formaldehyde. The workers must commence at the end farthest from the door and work backwards as the fumes are unpleasant, even dangerous at high concentrations. After sterilizing, the house is closed tightly for one day and if possible the temperature raised to about 70°F. The house is then fully opened for at least 14 days or until every trace of smell has gone. If the house adjoins others care must be taken that no fumes penetrate into them as they are fatal to plants. Clinkers or chippings on the benches can be removed and sterilized by steam if a sterilizer is at hand.

In changing over from unsterilized to sterilized composts it is better to clear one whole house at a time and sterilize it as above, so that a perfectly clean start is made. Thereafter not a single plant in a dirty pot or unsterilized soil should be brought into the house but only clean plants in clean soil. If a good start is made in this way, it is unlikely that pests or diseases will be encountered for some time. Nevertheless it is necessary to keep the sharpest watch for the first sign of an attack which, if promptly handled, can be controlled with ease.

POTS, PANS, ETC.

Dirty pots and pans should be scrubbed in water, paying special attention to the insides. They may be sterilized by putting them into cold water and bringing it to the boil for a minute or two. Alternatively they may be sterilized by dipping in a solution of 2 per cent. formaldehyde, i.e. 1 pint to 6 gallons of water, and afterwards stacked in an open place to allow the fumes to disperse. Crocks and seed trays (flats) may be sterilized similarly. Pots, pans, etc., sterilized by formaldehyde must on no account be used until every trace of smell has gone.

CULTURAL OPERATIONS

Cultural operations play an important part in maintaining the health of the plants.

The surface of seed pans should be perfectly level, so that seeds will not get washed to one place where they may germinate thickly and be in greater danger of damping off. Seed pans should be watered well before sowing, in time to allow surplus water to drain away.* After sowing, lightly sprinkle the surface with the finest rose-can, just enough to moisten the covering soil. In this way the danger of washing the seeds about will be avoided. Further waterings of seed pans should be made with a *fine* rose-can. The dipping of pans into water is not recommended as a general practice.

In pricking out the rule should be, do it early so that the first small root, the radicle, is removed intact and unbroken. Broken roots mean wounds where disease organisms can penetrate and establish themselves with ease, quite apart from the check the plant must suffer until new roots have formed. The radicle should not be more than $\frac{1}{2}$ to $\frac{3}{4}$ of an inch long when the seedling is pricked off.

* If the seed pans are not more than 2 ins. deep overall, one large crock over the hole is all that is required for drainage.

Seedlings to be pricked off and boxed plants to be potted off should be thoroughly watered some hours before they are dealt with. A plant shifted on with dry roots and an insufficient water content suffers a bad check. Watering-in should not be delayed for long or the peat in the compost may dry out so much as to be difficult to moisten again. In the first potting the soil should be firmed only a little; in each subsequent shift the new soil should be made a little firmer than that of the old ball.

PESTS AND DISEASES

Correct temperatures, illumination, humidity and watering will do a great deal towards keeping plants in a healthy and vigorous condition. Thus damping-off of seedlings may be encouraged by either careless watering or too humid an atmosphere, while red spider and thrips are encouraged by too dry conditions.

Even the best cultivated plants may be attacked by both pests and diseases, for reasons beyond the grower's control. Should this happen, only a few materials are necessary to combat them. Three types of insecticides, nicotine, derris and eucalyptus oil will control the pests. Nicotine is the most effective control for aphis and thrips; a good derris spray will eliminate aphis and red spider, while white fly and leaf-hoppers can be controlled by successive sprayings with a eucalyptus oil spray. Vaporized nicotine will control aphis and vaporized sulphur mites and red spider.

Cheshunt compound will prevent the spread of some forms of "damping-off" in seed pans although it will not cure plants already diseased. Rusts can best be controlled by using one of the proprietary brands of colloidal sulphur or copper which have many advantages over the home made fungicide. Vaporized sulphur, or finely ground sulphur used as a dust will control mildew.

The majority of pests and diseases can be kept in check by the regular use of fumigants and sprays. See that the staff can recognize the first symptoms of attack by such pests as red spider, thrips and leaf-hoppers and the early symptoms of such diseases as rust and mildew. A little time spent in instructing the men may save a whole house of plants from dis-figuration, besides economising materials, time and labour.

If it can possibly be avoided, plants should not be moved from one glasshouse to another if they are known to be diseased or infested, however slightly with disease or insect pests. If plants must be moved then spray them thoroughly on the previous day.

CUTTINGS

Cuttings and propagating frames need special care and must at all times be kept meticulously clean: rotting leaves and dead cuttings should be removed at once before they infect their neighbours. Picking over should not be relegated to Saturday mornings, but the gardener should remove any dead and diseased parts as soon as he notices them.

If the water supply is suspect in regard to its purity, then as an alternative it is almost always better to use mains water. We have never been able to detect the slightest difference in the use of the hard London mains water and the soft rain water collected from the glasshouse roofs. Both give the same results with the John Innes composts.

CHAPTER 14

QUALITIES OF THE JOHN INNES COMPOSTS

THE John Innes composts have certain properties, not commonly associated with seed and potting composts, to which reference will now be made.

Physical condition. By reason of the nature and proportion of the peat employed, the moisture content is exceptionally well regulated, rapid fluctuations from wet to dry being avoided. This also means that the labour of watering is reduced.

Rate of Growth. At normal temperatures, it will be found that plants grow much quicker in the new as compared with the old composts. At temperatures from five to ten degrees Fahrenheit lower than usual, growth will proceed at the normal rate in the John Innes composts. Thus the capacity of the house per annum is considerably increased in the first case, and fuel saved in the second. For example when grown at the usual temperature, main-crop tomatoes in the John Innes composts are ready for putting into $3\frac{1}{2}$ inch pots at four weeks from sowing, and are planted out at eight weeks. Alternatively they may be grown at temperatures averaging five degrees lower and will then be ready for planting out in the normal growing time of 10-12 weeks. Shortening of the growing period is due in part to the rapidity of seedling growth, and in part to the absence of any check after pricking-off and potting. The plant at once makes new roots and goes on growing as if it had not been disturbed (Fig. 17). Growers should allow for this in their timing of plants for flowering, etc., though the plants whose

Fig. 17.—*Verbena*. Comparisons between seed composts

Left :   average seed compost
Right :   John Innes Seed Compost

Note rapid root development in the new compost

flowering depends upon the season and length of day are not necessarily affected.

Disease resistance. On several occasions research workers have reported that the spread of disease

organisms in sterilized soil that has become infected
has been found to be substantially greater than in unsterilized soil, and warnings have been issued on the
need for the greatest care to prevent re-contamination.
With regard to the desirability of taking all precaution
to avoid re-contamination we are in complete agree-
ment. However, only a very short time must elapse
before sterilized soil is re-contaminated by spores of
all sorts of disease organisms; potting sheds and glass-
houses are in the nature of things sources of re-infection.
Nevertheless, it is a fact that disease is conspicuously
absent when the John Innes composts are used. By
way of example, "damping-off" has become a thing
of the past at Merton. It is so rare that although many
tens of thousands of seedlings are raised through the
year, 12 to 18 months may elapse before one small
patch is encountered. Growers raising plants in John
Innes composts under less hygienic conditions have
also reported disease to be greatly reduced. In view
of the above it seems that in those cases where re-
contamination of sterilized soil has led to increase
of disease, the physical condition and especially
the nutritional balance of the soil must have been
upset by the methods of sterilization and composting.
We must conclude, therefore, that the good physical
condition and nutritional balance of the John Innes
composts are a strong preventative of disease.

Further, plants grown in the new composts are less
susceptible to physiological disturbances induced by
bad environmental conditions. For example, as the
result of an accident, plants of cucumber and tomato
in an ordinary compost were rather severely damaged

by fumes from hot water pipes painted with a mixture of linseed oil and lamp-black, whereas the plants in the John Innes composts growing with them were practically unharmed. A similar result was found in regard to the susceptibility of cucumbers to sulphur fumes.

In winter time, with short days, fog and bad light, the contrast between the growth of the plants in the old and new composts is at a maximum.

For instance, in past years the authors, along with many other gardeners in foggy districts like London, found that the greatest of care was necessary with autumn sown plants of *Salpiglossis*, *Schizanthus*, Stocks, etc. The prevailing idea in regard to the winter cultivation of plants such as these was that the seeds must be sown early enough to get established plants before the arrival of the short winter days, after which no further growth was made until February. Watering was done with a certain amount of trepidation and a percentage of deaths was regarded as inevitable. In the new composts the same species grow steadily right through the winter, so that casualties now would be the result of bad cultivation.

Further to the above remarks tests made with tomato showed that the plants will grow vigorously at temperatures low enough to bring them to a complete standstill in the old composts. It may be remarked here that the foliage of plants grown in the new composts is not quite so deep a green as usual, and this at first suggests that they are "soft". Actually they are much "harder" than in the case of plants with greener foliage.

The Quality of the Loam

Growers have often asked if, using the cheaper loams as they sometimes must, they can expect to get as good results as we do at Merton. The answer is, not quite ; but their loams will go farther and give relatively better results if used to make the J.I. composts. The difference in composition of the loams is so far overbalanced on the physical side by the peat, and on the chemical side by the fertilizers, that the differences between loams are largely smoothed out and disappear.

This does not mean that the grower can neglect the question of quality when buying his loam ; he should always use the best procurable. It does mean, however, that he is made much more independent of the inevitable variations in the quality of loams and in consequence he can secure greater uniformity in the growth of his crops.

In illustration of the above points may be mentioned the results we have had from the use of the garden soil at Merton for raising seedlings and growing pot plants. Our soil is a black, light soil of rather poor quality. Dung and fertilizers have been applied over a good many years so that in some respects its manurial value is greater than that of the virgin loam used for potting, but it is much inferior to anything a grower would choose for pot plants. Nevertheless, germination and growth in sterilized and fertilized garden soil was almost as good as that which we obtained in the standard composts.

Fig. 18.—*Cineraria*. In the John Innes Potting Compost, stable-manure is successfully replaced by peat and fertilizers. . On the left John Innes Compost; on the right 7 loam, 3 manure, 2 sand

REPLACEMENT OF DUNG

In the new composts dung is replaced by peat and fertilizers without any loss of quality in the growth of

Fig. 19.—*Geraniums.* Cuttings struck in Autumn in John Innes Potting Compost, photographed early in March

[*by courtesy of Messrs. Ayres & Card, Ewell, Surrey*

plants (Fig. 18). Although the peat is of practically no manurial value, it plays an important part in replacing dung in composts. Dung has two distinctive qualities: it supplies small amounts of plant foods and is a bulky soil conditioner. In the John Innes composts the bulky conditioner is the peat and large amounts of plant foods are supplied by the fertilizers. One other point may be mentioned here. It is now very clear why the practice of adding bone meal to potting composts was, and is, so widespread, namely, because an abundant supply of phosphate is indispensable for good growth. As we have shown, however, superphosphate is superior in all respects to bone meal, which will certainly be replaced in the same way that dung will be replaced.

CUTTINGS

Although the John Innes composts were not devised for propagating purposes a good many species can be rooted from cuttings in the seed compost. Some stronger kinds, such as geranium can be struck in the potting compost (Fig. 19), but it is more often an advantage to add extra sand to either compost when using it for this purpose. The use of sterilized soils for cuttings helps to eliminate rotting off of the stems due to fungi normally present in the soil. For cuttings which do not do well in the presence of fertilizers, a useful propagating medium is :—

1 part by bulk sterilized loam.
2 parts by bulk good peat.
3 parts by bulk sterilized sand.

The loam and peat should be sifted through a $\frac{1}{4}$ inch riddle.

CHAPTER 15

THE NEW SIMPLICITY

IN the rst chapter of this book we discussed the confusion of ideas and practices regarding seed and potting composts. In the succeeding chapters we have endeavoured to straighten out this tangle and to provide a clear and reasoned basis for composting. We have shown that *standardization of materials and methods is not only possible but well worth while*.

It makes for economy, as a lesser number of materials, each unvarying and dependable, are used to replace others of doubtful value.

It makes for simplicity, since the composts can be mixed in advance and drawn from as required, instead of making separate mixtures for each kind of plant at each stage of its growth.

It makes for certainty. The grower does not have to trust to soil mixtures differing in quality, according to the materials used or the persons making them up. He knows he has a compost which will give him consistent and uniform results. The element of risk is thus reduced.

Further, in an unvarying compost, growth is also unvarying as far as soil conditions are concerned, and where growth is uniform it is possible to estimate the cultural requirements (e.g. times of potting on) more exactly.

In addition to the benefits of standardization,

there must be added those derived from the use of balanced fertilizers and properly sterilized soil. The growth of plants raised in the John Innes composts is of the highest quality (Fig. 20), because all soil pests and diseases are eliminated and there is a good supply of food from the moment of germination onwards. Growth

Fig. 20.—*Streptocarpus* " Merton Giant ". A batch of 200 plants grown in the John Innes Potting Compost and fed with the John Innes Feed. The plants are in 3½-inch pots

is sturdy and disease resistant and even when the plants are put into poorer soil (as when bedding out of doors) they get over the shift quicker and grow away more rapidly. The growing of plants in standardized soil is nothing new, of course. Most gardens have shrubs

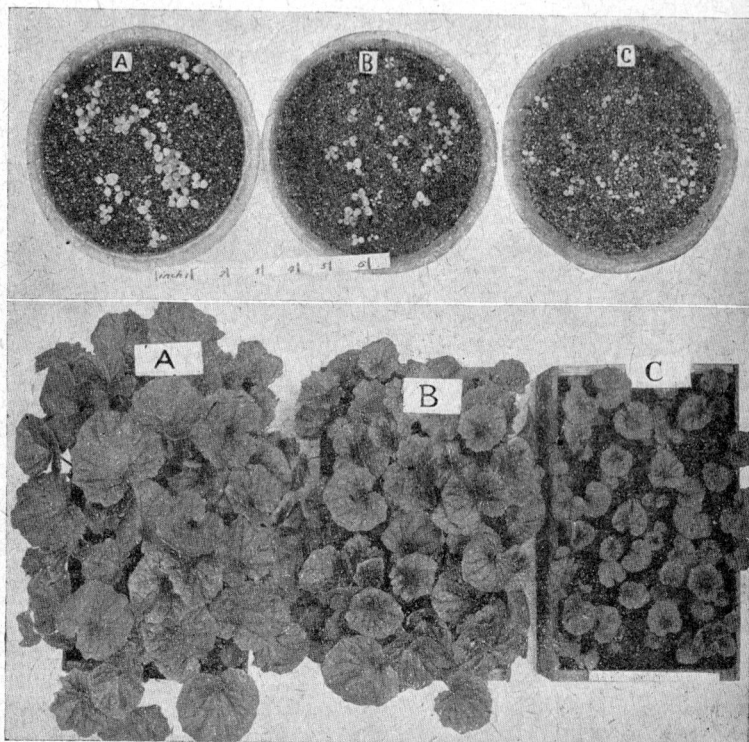

Fig. 21.—*Cineraria*. Showing improved growth in sterilized and fertilized seed composts

Top: shortly after germination. Bottom : the same plants at a later stage

A. sterilized and fertilized (John Innes Compost)
B. fertilized only.   C. unsterilized and unfertilized

and trees, bulbs, alpine and herbaceous plants all growing in the same soil out-of-doors, and these same plants can be grown quite satisfactorily in fairly different soils. Even under glass some commercial growers have for many years used one or two composts for a variety of plants. What is new about the John Innes composts is the addition of fertilizers to the *seed* compost (Fig. 21), the use of *balanced* fertilizers at each stage of the plant's life and the *method* of soil sterilization.

Again it must not be thought that these composts are the best possible for all plants. By taking one species at a time and studying that one's special requirements, it would be easy to devise a compost ideally suited to it: but such a compost would not necessarily be suitable for other species. Standardization as we conceive it, is a compromise which aims at getting first rate results with the greatest number of species. It is a compromise, however, which has been amply justified in practice.

A great variety of hardy and tender plants have been grown successfully by ourselves and other growers in the new composts. So far, no plant has been found which will not grow well in the John Innes composts. It is not expected, of course, that they would be suitable for highly specialized subjects such as the epiphytic orchids.

The following lists are by no means complete, but will serve to indicate the wide range of species that we have successfully grown in the John Innes composts.

Cool greenhouse plants :

Agapanthus	Browallia
Arum	Calceolaria
Asparagus fern	Camellia
Azalea	Capsicum
Bouvardia	Carnation
	Cacti

Celosia
Chrysanthemum
Cineraria
Crassula
Cyclamen
Cypripedium
Erica (3 species)
Fuchsia
Genista
Gerbera
Hydrangea
Kalanchoe
Maidenhair fern
Marguerite
Myosotis
Nephrolepis
Primula
Richardia
Rose
Salpiglossis
Sansevieria
Schizanthus
Solanum
Statice
Torenia

Warm greenhouse plants :
Achimenes
Anthurium
Aroids
Begonia species
Begonia (winter flowering)
Caladium
Canna
Clerodendron
Croton
Dracaena
Exacum
Gardenia
Gloriosa
Glorinia

Grevillea
Hoya
Ixora
Nepenthes
Pandanus
Palms
Peperomia
Pilea
Platycerium
Saintpaulia
Streptocarpus
Vriesia

Bedding plants :
Abutilon
Alyssum
Antirrhinum
Aster (China)
Ageratum
Begonia
Calendula
Centaurea
Coleus
Coreopsis
Cosmos
Echeveria
Eucalyptus
Gazania
Grevillea
Heliotrope
Humea
Kochia
Lisianthus
Lobelia
Mesembryanthemum
Mimulus
Nemesia
Nicotiana
Petunia
Pelargonium
Phlox

Polyanthus
Portulaca
Ricinus
Salpiglossis
Salvia
Statice
Sweet Pea
Tagetes
Verbena
Viola
Zinnia

Herbaceous plants :
Anchusa
Aquilegia
Aster (Michaelmas daisies)
Campanula
Dahlia
Dierama
Delphinium
Heuchera
Incarvillea
Lupin
Paeonia
Papaver
Penstemon
Phlox
Platycodon
Plumbago
Pyrethrum
Scabious
Sidalcea
Thalictrum
Verbascum

Bulbs :
Amaryllis
Babiana
Camassia
Freesia

Hyacinth
Iris
Lachenalia
Lilium
Narcissus
Nerine
Ornithogalum
Tulip

Alpine plants :
Aethionema
Anacyclus
Androsace
Aubrieta
Campanula
Daphne
Dianthus
Gentiana
Erica carnea
        ciliaris
        mediterranea
        vagans
Haberlea
Helichrysum
Lithospermum
Lewisia
Meconopsis
Morisea
Nierembergia
Onosma
Origanum
Phyteuma
Primula
Ramondia
Roscoea
Saxifrage
Sempervivum
Zauschneria

Trees and Shrubs :
Many hardy species including

Clematis
Conifers
Cytisus
Erica Veitchii
        terminalis
Fabiana
Rose
   etc.

Fruits :
Aubergine
Blackberry
Cucumber
Currant
Gooseberry
Raspberry
Tomato
Fruit trees in pots

Vegetables :
Beans
Cauliflower
Celery
Leeks
Lettuce
Maize
Onions
Parsley

TABLES, ETC.

Analysis of fertilizers used in the John Innes Composts :

Hoof and horn ($\frac{1}{8}$ in. fine grist) approx. 13% nitrogen.

Superphosphate   ,,   18% phosphoric acid.

Sulphate of potash   ,,   48% potash.

Analysis of John Innes Base Fertilizer as used in the potting composts :
Nitrogen 5·1% : Phosphoric acid 7·2% : Potash 9·7 %.

Seed Compost	super-phosphate	chalk or limestone
To 1 bushel add	$1\frac{1}{2}$ oz.	$\frac{3}{4}$ oz.
4 bushels ,, ...	6 oz.	3 oz.
8 bushels ,, ...	$\frac{3}{4}$ lb.	6 oz.
$\frac{1}{2}$ cu. yard ,, ...	1 lb.	$\frac{1}{2}$ lb.
1 cu. yard ,, ...	2 lb.	1 lb.

Potting Compost	hoof and horn	super-phosphate	sulphate of potash	chalk or limestone
To 1 bushel	$1\frac{1}{2}$ oz.	$1\frac{1}{2}$ oz.	$\frac{3}{4}$ oz.	$\frac{3}{4}$ oz.
4 bushels	6 oz.	6 oz.	3 oz.	3 oz.
8 bushels	$\frac{3}{4}$ lb.	$\frac{3}{4}$ lb.	6 oz.	6 oz.
$\frac{1}{2}$ cu. yard	1 lb.	1 lb.	$\frac{1}{2}$ lb.	$\frac{1}{2}$ lb.
1 cu. yard	2 lb.	2 lb.	1 lb.	1 lb.

Sizes of flower pots :

terms used	diameter in inches	depth in inches
Thimbles	2	 2
Thumbs	$2\frac{1}{2}$	.... $2\frac{1}{2}$
60's	3	.... $3\frac{1}{2}$
48's	$4\frac{1}{2}$	 5
32's	6	 6
24's	$8\frac{1}{2}$	 8
16's	$9\frac{1}{2}$	 9
12's	$11\frac{1}{2}$	 10
8's	12	 11
6's	13	 12
4's	15	 13
2's	18	 14

One bushel of compost is sufficient to pot :—

    90 to 100 plants in 60 sized pots.
    40 to 45 plants in 48 sized pots.
    45 to 50 plants potted from thumbs to 48's.
    50 to 55 plants potted from 60's to 48's.
    20 to 25 plants potted from 60's to 32's.
    16 to 18 plants potted from 48's to 24's.

Pot sizes vary and these figures are only approximate.

The nursery seed tray measures 14 × $8\frac{1}{2}$ inches inside.

Nine shallow trays (2 ins.) or six deep trays (3 ins.) can be prepared from a bushel of soil.

The nursery seed tray holds :—

    40 plants : 5 rows of 8 at $1\frac{3}{4} \times 1\frac{3}{4}$ inches apart.
    54 plants : 6   ,, ,, 9 at $1\frac{1}{2} \times 1\frac{1}{2}$ inches apart.
    60 plants : 6   ,, ,, 10 at $1\frac{1}{4} \times 1\frac{1}{4}$ inches apart.

Liquid feeding :—

> 100 plants in 60's will take 1½ gallons of liquid feed.
> 100 plants in 48's will take 2 gallons of liquid feed.
> 100 plants of 32's will take 5 gallons of liquid feed.

To ascertain the capacity of circular tanks :—

> Multiply in feet half the circumference by half the diameter by the depth and multiply the result by 6¼ to give the capacity in gallons.

To ascertain the capacity of rectangular tanks :—

> Multiply in feet the length by the width by the depth and multiply the result by 6¼ to give the capacity in gallons.

Measures of Capacity :

> 1 gallon $= 277\frac{1}{4}$ cubic inches.
> 6¼ gallons $= 1$ cubic foot.
> 1 bushel $= 2,220$ cubic inches.
> 8 gallons $= 1$ bushel.
> 21 bushels $= 1$ cubic yard.

A rectangular box 22 ins. long, 10 ins. wide and 10 ins. deep holds one bushel of soil.

Thermometers.

> To change Fahrenheit readings into Centigrade readings subtract 32, multiply by 5, and divide by 9.
> To change Centigrade readings to Fahrenheit readings multiply by 9, divide by 5 and add 32.

E*

INDEX